With love for

for 1978

from

Joan.

RENAISSANCE FORTIFICATION

ART OR ENGINEERING?

THIS IS THE EIGHTH OF THE
WALTER NEURATH MEMORIAL LECTURES
WHICH ARE GIVEN ANNUALLY EACH SPRING ON
SUBJECTS REFLECTING THE INTERESTS OF
THE FOUNDER
OF THAMES AND HUDSON

THE DIRECTORS WISH TO EXPRESS
PARTICULAR GRATITUDE TO THE GOVERNORS AND
MASTER OF BIRKBECK COLLEGE
UNIVERSITY OF LONDON
FOR THEIR GRACIOUS SPONSORSHIP OF
THESE LECTURES

RENAISSANCE FORTIFICATION

ART OR ENGINEERING?

J. R. HALE

THAMES AND HUDSON

Printed and bound in Great Britain by Jarrold and Sons Ltd, Norwich

The feeling of the latest Walter Neurath lecturer must be mixed: alarm – at the thought of the distinction of his predecessors; gratitude – for a freedom obtainable in no other form for the adequate illustration of a briefly expressed but deeply felt enthusiasm; but, most of all, pleasure – that very special pleasure that comes from delivering a lecture connected by name with the memory of a man who did so much both for the scholarship and the popularization of history and art.

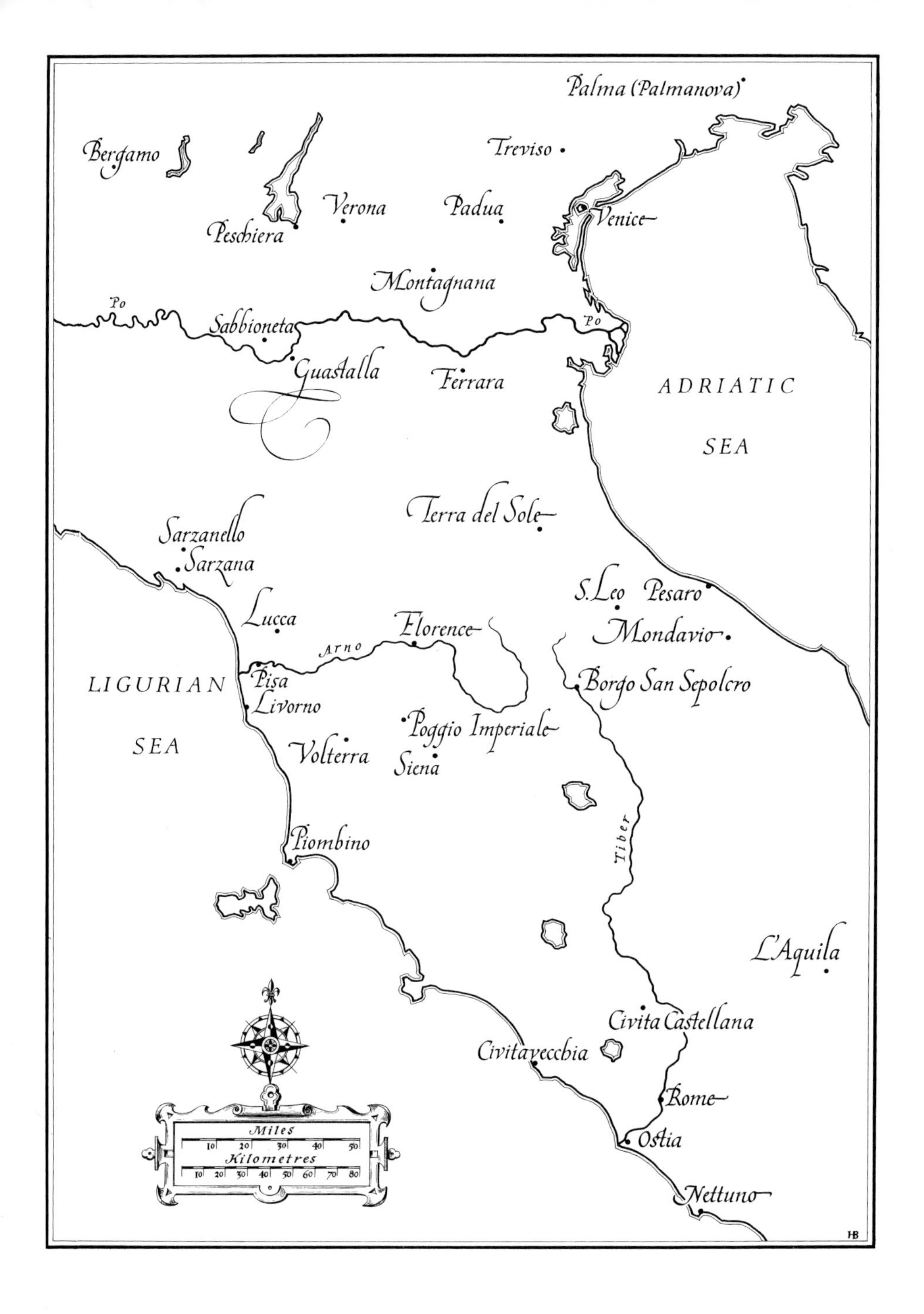
Palma (Palmanova)
Treviso
Bergamo
Verona
Padua
Venice
Peschiera
Montagnana
Po
Sabbioneta
Po
Guastalla
Ferrara
ADRIATIC
SEA
Terra del Sole
Sarzanello
Sarzana
S. Leo
Pesaro
Lucca
Florence
Mondavio
Arno
Pisa
LIGURIAN
Borgo San Sepolcro
Livorno
Poggio Imperiale
SEA
Volterra
Siena
Tiber
Piombino
L'Aquila
Civita Castellana
Civitavecchia
Rome
Miles
10 20 30 40 50
Kilometres
10 20 30 40 50 60 70 80
Ostia
Nettuno
HB

THE TRANSFORMATION of the styles in which churches and palaces were built during the Renaissance was accompanied by a revolution in the design of fortifications. The explosive mine and gunpowder artillery led to the supplanting of the 'picturesque' castle [1] by the sterner fortress or citadel, of the towered wall [2] by the squat bastioned trace. The principles underlying this revolution evolved in Italy during the fifteenth and remained valid until the early nineteenth century; they conditioned the appearance and development of towns and cities not only elsewhere in Europe but in America, Africa and Asia [4]. Yet in the mainstream of architectural history fortifications are accorded but a fitful or embarrassed attention. They are historically important, but are they, can they be, beautiful? Are they a proper concern for the historian of art, or should they be left to that perhaps drabber figure, the chronicler of engineering?[1]

To those who saw them being built these questions would have been meaningless. And on the assumption that our own appreciation will be enhanced by an understanding of how fortifications were planned and how they were regarded at the time, I shall devote myself chiefly to the Renaissance, and, to keep the subject within bounds, to Italy.

As far as I know, only one Renaissance architect, Girolamo Genga, disparaged military at the expense of civic and religious architecture. When the first Genoese castellan took over the reconstructed fortress of Sarzanello [3] in 1502 he declared it 'very strong and beautiful'.[2] Vasari described Sanmicheli's fortress of S. Andrea in the Venetian lagoon [5] as 'marvellous; . . . with the beauty of its walls it represents the grandeur and majesty of the most famous buildings of [ancient] Roman greatness'. What it represents now, having been neglected to the point of collapse, is the timeliness, indeed the urgency of the question posed in the title of this lecture.

1 Francesco di Giorgio, 'retardataire' tower at Mondavio, 1490–2

2 Montagnana, the medieval town wall

3 Francione and Luca del Caprina, Sarzanello, 1493–1502

4 Diu, the ex-Portuguese Indian fortress

5 MICHELE SANMICHELI, fortress of S. Andrea, Venice, designed 1535

The revolution in the design of fortifications was a technological one. Yet all its main features can be illustrated from the work of artists: men best known as painters, sculptors or the designers of churches or palaces.

In 1433 Brunelleschi's bastion at Pisa began the investigation of how to exploit flanking fire from artillery embrasures.[3] Laurana's *rocca* at Pesaro jettisoned the tall towers that had become vulnerable to gunfire, as did Francesco di Giorgio's massive hilltop fortress of S. Leo. At Civitacastellana [33] Antonio da San Gallo the Elder dropped the machicolations that had also become vulnerable and with them gave up the notion of vertical, 'drop on the head' defence, relying, as did Giuliano da San Gallo at Poggio Imperiale [32], on flanking fire between bastions; these, as in the central defence of Bramante's fortress at Civitavecchia [30], were pointed, the shape that was soon to supplant the round bastion.[4] This process was encouraged by bastions like those of Peruzzi at Siena; confirmed by the widely discussed Ardeatino bastion at Rome of Antonio da San Gallo the Younger [6]; and

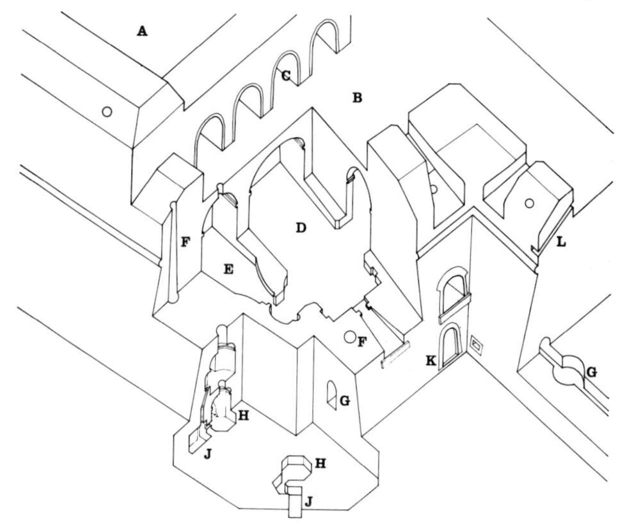

6 ANTONIO DA SAN GALLO THE YOUNGER, Ardeatino bastion, Rome, 1542

KEY

A cavalier (upper gun platform)
B *piazza* (platform for large guns)
C vaulted bomb shelters
D casemate (chamber for smaller guns)
E magazine
F ventilation flues
G countermine gallery
H *pozzi* (well shafts)
J countermine shafts
K sally port
L low-angle embrasure for firing at ground close to walls

7 Florence from the Belvedere fortress, 1590–5

deployed with the confidence of orthodoxy by Buontalenti in the Belvedere fortress in Florence [7].

With Arnolfo's cathedral and Giotto's campanile in view, the point needs no labouring. The tradition that artists and 'art' architects should turn naturally to fortification was an old one. Vasari's statement that Arnolfo designed the third circuit of Florence's walls has not been disproved. We have Giotto's contract of 1334 as their supervisor. Moreover, we know that the sculptor Andrea Pisano helped to complete them – and we have Benvenuto Cellini's word, at least, that he was one of those charged by Duke Cosimo I between 1552 and 1554 to update them. Before that, Florence diverted Leonardo da Vinci, recently Cesare Borgia's 'architect and engineer general', from his work on the *Battle of Anghiari* in the Palazzo Vecchio to inspect fortifications near Pisa and to design new ones at Piombino in 1503–4 [8], and appointed Michelangelo in 1529 'governor and procurator general of the fortifications' of the city [9].[5]

Versatility of this order justified Vasari's remark that 'we seldom find a man distinguishing himself in one branch of art who cannot readily acquire the knowledge of others which . . . proceed, as it were, from the same source'.[6] And I hope that it justifies my proposing to devote some time to exploring the circumstances in which men came to plan fortifications during the fifteenth and sixteenth centuries and, in particular, the repute in which they and their works were held.

The 'source' mentioned by Vasari as permitting a versatility of practice was, above all, *disegno*: a sense of design and a skill in drawing. There was no apprenticeship, no prescribed training for Renaissance architects. Nor was architecture looked on as a profession, though it was highly respected as an activity. The younger Antonio da San Gallo and Bartolomeo Genga are rare examples of men who learned to be architects from an uncle or a father. The others – to restrict myself to those who worked on fortifications – came to architecture from other pursuits which gave a training in *disegno*.[7] Brunelleschi and Peruzzi began as jewellers and goldsmiths. Francione, designer of the *rocca* at Volterra, started as a joiner specializing in intarsia work; as did Baccio Pontelli, architect of the *rocca* at Ostia. The casualness with which a skill in *disegno* could lead to architectural commissions emerges strikingly in Manetti's biography of Brunelleschi: 'since [as a jeweller] he revealed a marvellous genius, his advice about buildings was in great demand'. A century later Vasari described how the Viceroy Ferrante Gonzaga, impressed in Rome by the young portrait-painter Domenico Giutatalocchi and 'wanting to have a young man at his hand who might design and put on paper for him all that he was daily planning', took him to Sicily where he speedily graduated from drawing fortifications to designing them. Later still, Buontalenti, trained as a painter by Bronzino and Salviati, became the chief military engineer to

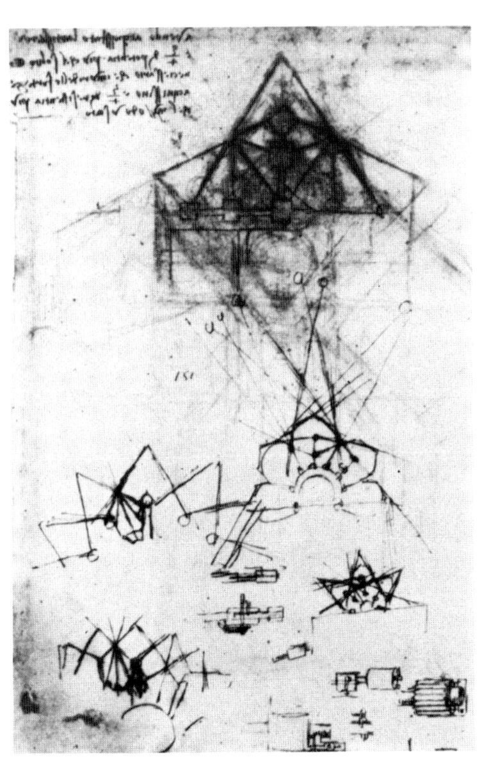

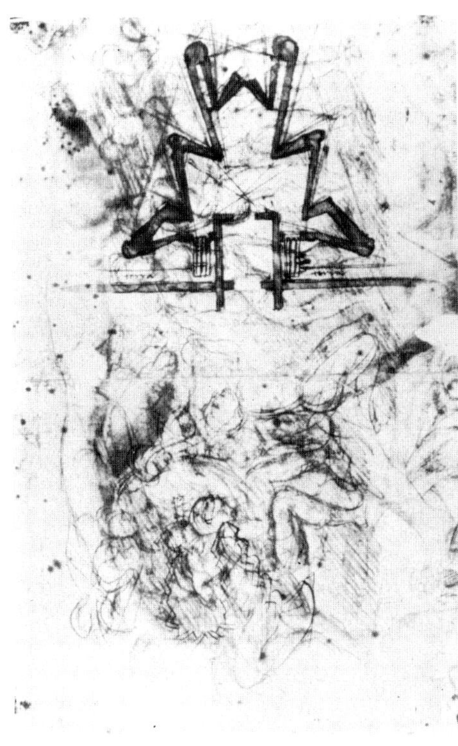

8 LEONARDO DA VINCI, sketches for Piombino, *c.* 1504
9 MICHELANGELO, design for wall of Florence, ?1526

successive dukes of Florence, wrote a treatise on military architecture and, while still justifying as master of ducal festivities his nickname 'Bernardo of the Catherine Wheels', died in 1608 leaving a litter of models and plans of fortifications[8] in the hands of his executors.

Not all Renaissance architects divided their attention in this way between the arts of peace and of war. Some, like Codussi and Sansovino, never had anything to do with fortifications; others, like Michelozzo, turned to them only after long careers as civil architects; others, like Cronaca, were simply called in as consultants: and others, like Palladio, did not believe in the practical value of military

10 Bernardo Poccetti (d. 1612), a military architect's workshop

architecture at all. There were some architects who were chiefly employed on military works, like the Florentine Cecca. And from Taccola in the fifteenth century to Antonio Lupicini in the sixteenth there were specialists in hydraulics, land reclamation and machines who were called in to construct fortifications but never given a civic commission.

This variety of emphases, however, was the result chiefly of the availability of commissions, partly of temperament, hardly at all of a training that implied specialization. *Disegno* carries no such implication. Neither did the other prerequisite Alberti had coupled with it: mathematics. These were the two skills an architect 'can no more be without than a poet can be without the knowledge of feet and syllables'.[9] A century later Pietro Cataneo, in his book on civil and military architecture,[10] pointed to the need for geometry and arithmetic in calculating proportions, quantities and costs, and *disegno* for providing plans, elevations and bird's-eye views [11, 12]. Both attainments feature in an account of Michele Sanmicheli's visit in 1531 to Alessandria, which Duke Francesco Sforza II had asked him to report on with a

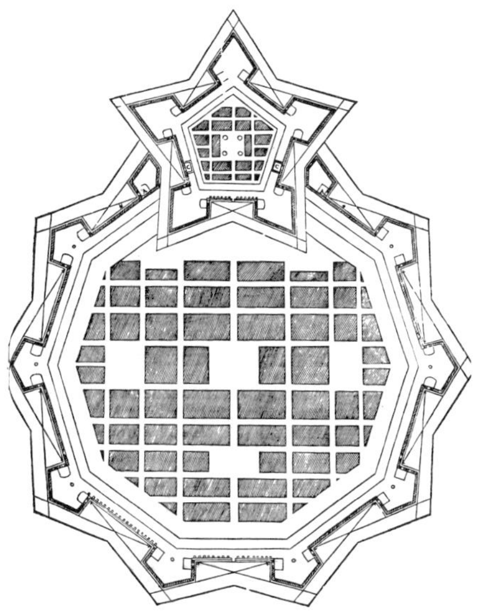

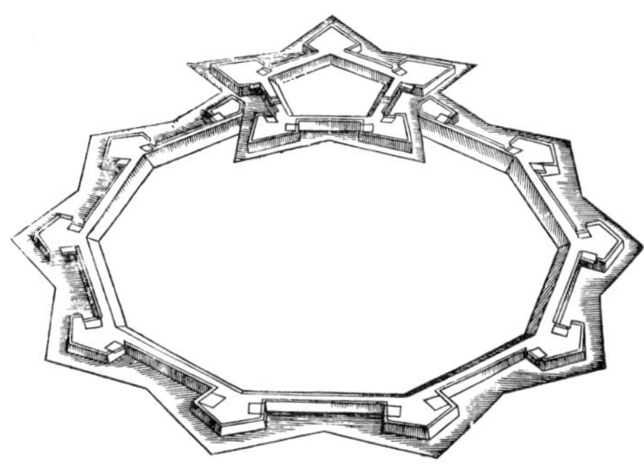

11, 12 PIETRO CATANEO, project for town walls, plan and perspective view, 1554

13 BACCIO PONTELLI, part of *rocca* at Ostia, and church of S. Aurea, 1463–6

14 Rome, part of fortifications of the Borgo

view to modernizing its walls. 'On arriving, Maestro Michele several times went round the site measuring it, then he got down to drawing, first in the form it has now, then, after making a separate sketch showing the additions he proposed for making it as strong as possible, he made a further survey to check the levels of the ground with a view to an effectual defence against mines.' Finally, Francesco's agent reported, he produced 'some finished drawings' to show to the Duke.[11]

Sanmicheli was then briefly on secondment from his post as 'engineer in charge of buildings' in Verona. Previously he had worked on the façade of the cathedral of Orvieto and designed a funerary chapel in the church of S. Domenico there. The word 'engineer', however, was, when it came to the design and construction of buildings, virtually interchangeable with 'architect'. Laurana's contract of 1468 for the new ducal palace at Urbino started with a praise of architecture and then named him as 'engineer and overseer'. While Biagio Rossetti was working on the churches, palaces and walls of the Herculanean Addition at Ferrara he was referred to almost in alternate documents as

'architect' and 'engineer'. Pontelli's official title was 'engineer in chief' but he firmly signed himself 'architect' on the *rocca* at Ostia – where, indeed, he had laid out the adjoining *piazza* and designed its church [13]. In two famous consultations in the middle of the sixteenth century, one to discuss Paul III's re-fortification of the Borgo in Rome [14], the other to plan Margaret Farnese's palace in Piacenza, a mixture of predominantly military and predominantly civil architects was present.

Indeed, rather than military engineers contaminating the image of architecture, it was conceivably the other way about. Of fifteenth-century architects it has been said recently that 'there is little evidence that society generally had the high regard for them which we associate with the renaissance appreciation of artistic genius'.[12] If they were more respected, and more highly paid, in the following century, it was in part because of their association with the unprecedented surge of new fortifications that brought them into frequent contact with rulers and their viceroys and professional military advisers. The wars, the constant political uncertainty that followed the first French invasion of Italy in 1494, did much to enhance the reputation of the architecture of walls and citadels. Is it not this, asked the author of a treatise on fortification in 1557, 'that keeps men in a safe and quiet state? . . . Is it not this that permits the practice of all the other arts?'[13] It was the author of another treatise on military, not ecclesiastical, architecture, who dedicated his work in 1570 'to the praise, honour and glory of the Eternal and Supreme Architect'.[14]

Nor must we imagine the status of the engineer as architect as being diminished by his connection with the invention and construction of machines. Taccola was not simply justifying his own appetite for the ingenious contrivance when he described Brunelleschi as 'gifted by God especially in architecture, [and] a most learned inventor of devices in mechanics'.[15] Vasari did not have his tongue in his cheek when he traced three stages in the evolution of architecture: necessity, ornament, machinery; 'by which', he wrote, 'artists are compelled to prove their ingenuity and industry by the discovery of tractile forces, the invention of hydraulic machines, engines of war, catapults and every other sort of laborious contrivance which, under the name of architectural and warlike machinery, contribute to disconcert one's enemies . . . and render the world more beautiful and more enjoyable'.[16]

Both quotations echo the authority of Vitruvius, whose definition of architecture included 'the construction of machinery', and who wrote of himself: 'I was ready to supply and repair *ballistae*, *scorpiones* and other artillery.'[17]

From the discovery of a manuscript of his *De architectura* in 1415, the work both determined the definition of architecture and conditioned the self-training of architects. The dictum attributed to Michelangelo – 'if a man can draw, with the help of Vitruvius he can become a good architect'[18] – is at least *ben trovato*: a careful study of the *De architectura* turned the thirty-five-year-old wool merchant Giovanni Battista Belluzzi into a highly respected military engineer [17]. For, though the bulk of Vitruvius' treatise is concerned with civic and religious buildings, his criteria of excellence – durability, convenience and beauty – also apply to a city's fortified carapace, the walls and towers with which he begins. He exalts the other end of the military engineering spectrum when he says, in the concluding section dealing with offensive and defensive machines, that thanks to them 'the freedom of states has been preserved by the cunning of architects'. In manuscript after manuscript and then, after the *editio princeps* of the 1480s, in print, military and civil architecture were authoritatively tucked in together between the same sheets.

The first illustrated edition was produced in 1511 by the scholarly engineer-architect Fra Giocondo, who redesigned, in that same year, the fortifications of Padua and Treviso. The next, of 1521, carried an elaborate commentary by Cesariano which cited the new walls of Ferrara, S. Leo, and the Civitavecchia *rocca* of his master Bramante. The next, of 1536, was dedicated to a retired professional soldier.[19] It was not, however, until the edition of Daniele Barbaro in 1556 that a serious attempt was made to establish the extent to which Vitruvius' text had been made obsolete by the impact of gunpowder and the development of the bastion. With the help of striking new illustrations (including a flap that could be lifted to explain the construction of a bastion) Barbaro maintained the authority of Vitruvius' inclusion of military, as well as civil architecture, by bringing this part of his inquiry up to date [15, 16].

Meanwhile, to turn to Renaissance treatises on architecture, when Alberti wrote his *De re aedificatoria* in the 1440s he included as a matter of course – though on some issues he polemicized against Vitruvius – lengthy disquisitions on defensive walls and fortresses. He omitted mechanical devices but only 'inasmuch as I intend to treat of these military machines more clearly in another place'.[20] The next general treatise, that of Filarete, a sculptor and architect who had worked briefly on fortifications, likewise included walls and fortresses. Given the number of military commissions fulfilled by Francesco di Giorgio,[21] his

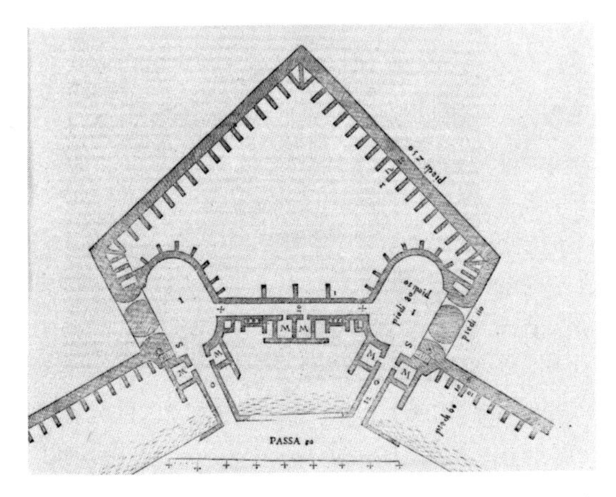

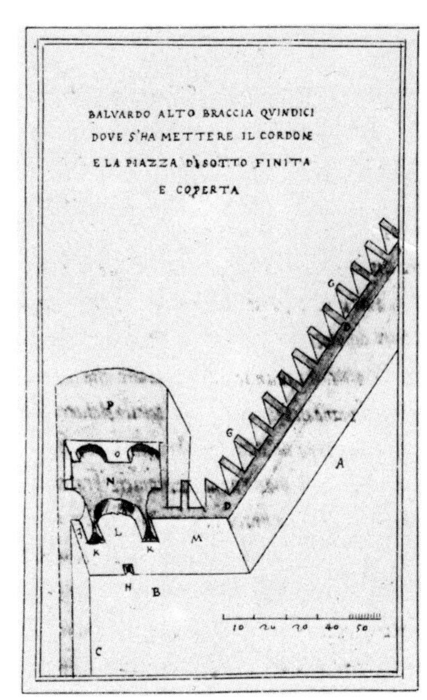

15, 16 Plan of the bastion from Daniele Barbaro's edition of Vitruvius, 1556; the same, with flap raised

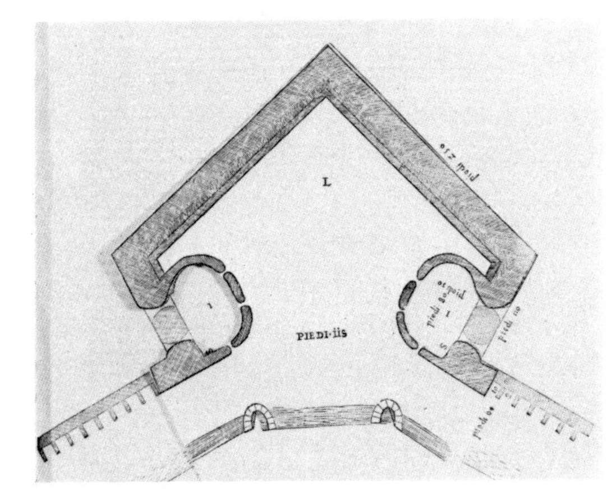

17 G. B. BELLUZZI, constructional drawing, face and flank of a bastion, *c.* 1545

tribute to the influence of Vitruvius can perhaps be seen in an opposite way: it comes as a surprise that his treatise of the 1490s, with so much of its space and its inventive energy devoted to fortifications, includes civic and ecclesiastical buildings at all. It has been increasingly surmised that Leonardo was contemplating a book on architecture; this, too, to judge from his notes and drawings, would have afforded a prominent, if not a predominant, place to fortifications among churches, palaces and town-plans.

With the notable exception of Palladio's *Quattro libri* . . ., and leaving aside books that were little more than collections of architectural patterns, Italian works on architecture, printed or unpublished, continued to include fortification as a matter of course. Thus Pietro Cataneo's *Quattro primi libri di architettura* devoted its first and longest book to military architecture. Serlio's printed work omitted it, but his unpublished 'eighth book' was devoted to military (albeit classical) camps.[22] The sculptor and villa architect Bartolomeo Ammannati's unfinished treatise on cities contained a severely practical section on fortifications.[23] Vasari the Younger's 1598 treatise on the ideal city struck a note of apology, it is true: do not be surprised, he wrote, that I deal first with fortifications, for without them 'the inhabitants could not attend divine worship, could not study or trade'.[24] But Scamozzi's very influential *Idea della architettura universale* of 1615 returned to Barbaro's principle of updating Vitruvius' section on walls and contained an enthusiastic, long and thoroughly practical section on military architecture [18].

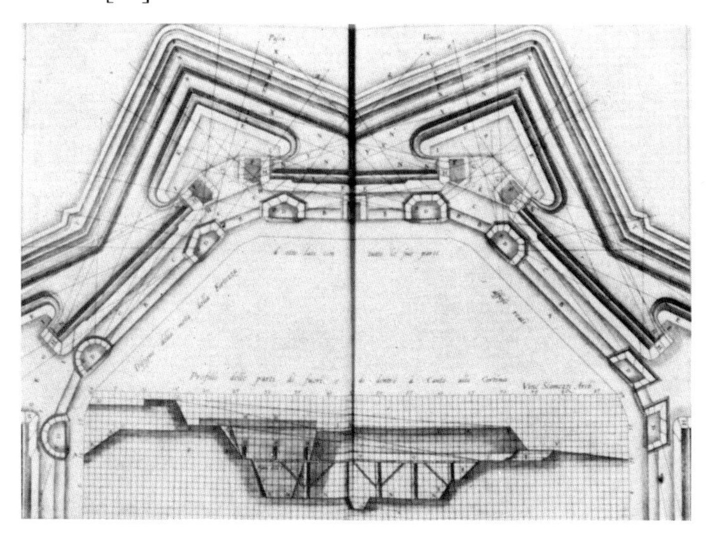

18 Vicenzo Scamozzi, plan and profile of part of bastioned front, 1615

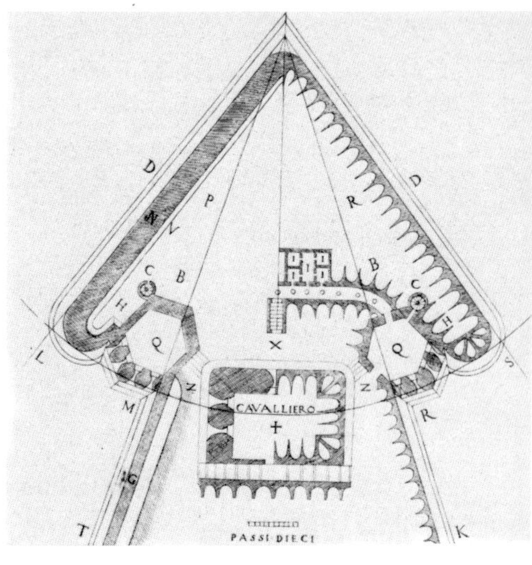

19 Nettuno, *rocca*, 1501–3
20 GALASSO ALGHISI, constructional plan of bastion, 1570

21 L'Aquila, *rocca*, *c.* 1535

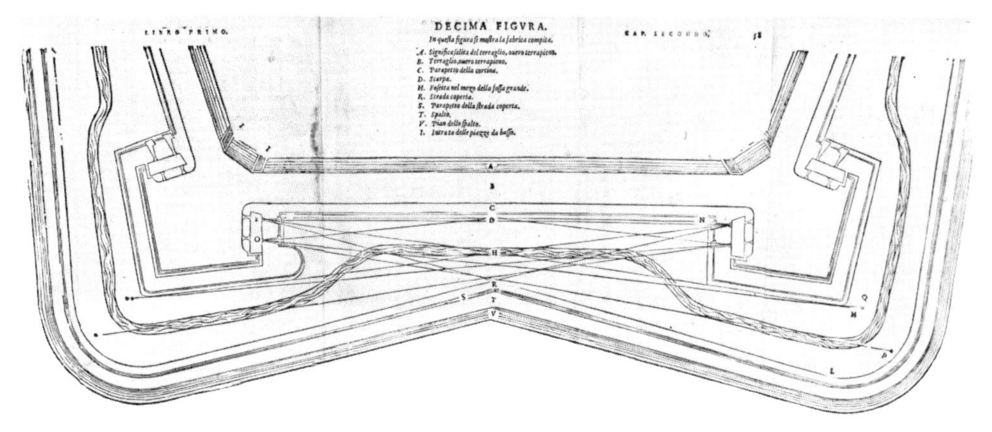

22 GIROLAMO CATANEO, bastions (one semi-lobed) and fire-plan, 1571

What is more, under the aegis of the revered Vitruvius, military architecture, stimulated by incessant experiment [19, 21], encouraged by political debate about the strategic and political functions of forts, walls and citadels, came to establish a literature of its own [20, 22]: seventeen works were published in Italy between 1554 and 1599. And civil architecture was outstripped not only in print but in prestige. 'In the sixteenth century,' Professor Kubler has noted, with evident distaste, 'military architects, like physicists today, were more in demand and more highly rewarded than their profane colleagues.'[25] In Girolamo Ruscelli's *Le imprese illustre* of 1580 the emblems and mottoes of two military architects, Zanchi and Lanteri, are shown among those of kings and cardinals; only two, but no civil architect at all is included. Francesco Tensini was made *cavaliere*; Francesco Paciotto was knighted as 'engineer general in Flanders' for Philip II, and ended as Count of Fonte Fabbri in his native Urbino after serving as 'architect general' to the Duke of Savoy. Paciotto was not simply rewarded on utilitarian grounds: the word 'architect' had not lost its implications of versatility and scholarship. As a young man he wrote a treatise on Vitruvius. In mid career he was called in to modify Vignola's plans for Caprarola and then to criticize Juan Bautista de Toledo's plans for parts of the Escorial, which he did in Vitruvian, and no uncertain, terms.

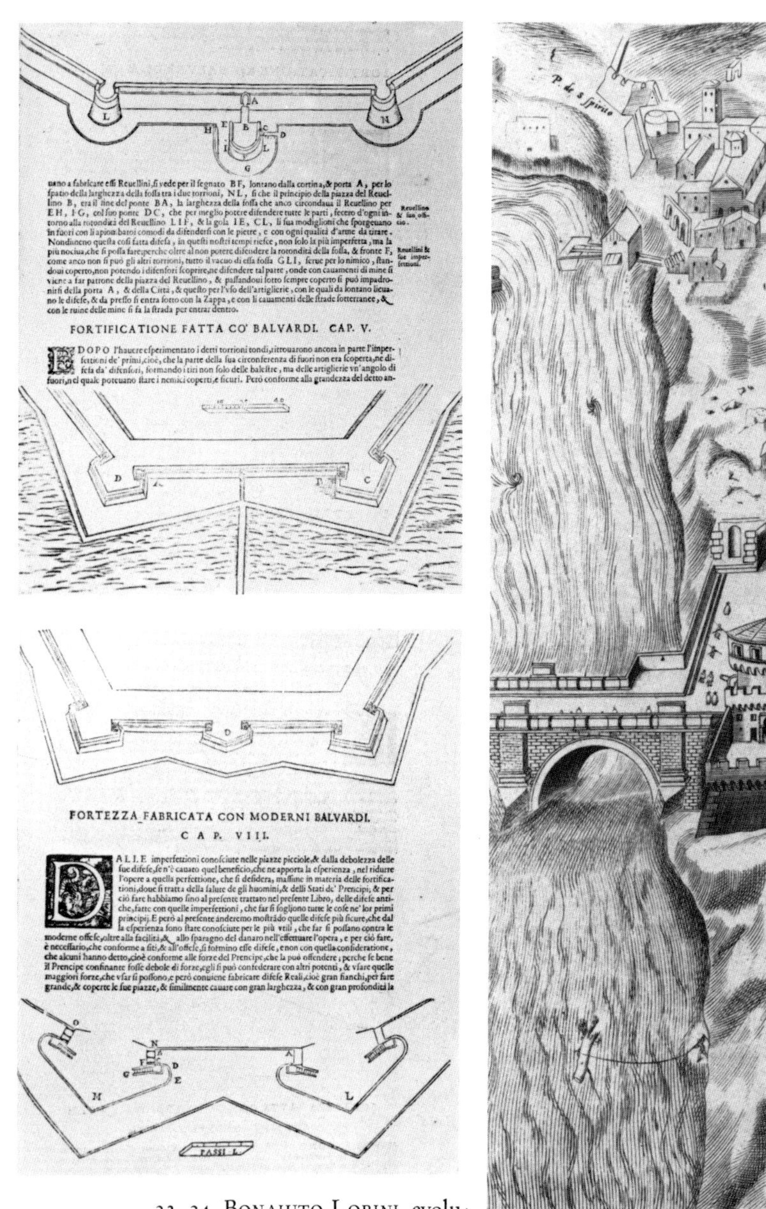

uano a fabricare essi Reuellini, si vede per il segnato BF, lontano dalla cortina, & porta A, per lo spatio della larghezza della fossa tra i due torrioni, NL, si che il principio della piazza del Reuellino B, era il fine del ponte BA, la larghezza della fossa che anco circondaua il Reuellino per EH, IG, col suo ponte DC, che per meglio potere difendere tutte le parti, fecero d'ogni intorno alla rotondità del Reuellino LIF, & la gola IE, CL, li sua modiglioni che sporgeuano in fuori con li apiombatoi comodi da difendersi con le pietre, e con ogni qualità d'arme da tirare. Nondimeno questa così fatta difesa, in questi nostri tempi riesce, non solo la più imperfetta, ma la più nociua, che si possa fare; perche oltre al non potere difendere la rotondità della fossa, & fronte F, come anco non si può gli altri torrioni, tutto il vacuo di essa fossa GLI, serue per lo nimico, standoui coperto, non potendo i difensori scoprire, ne difendere tal parte, onde con cauamenti di mine si viene a far patrone della piazza del Reuellino, & passandoui sotto sempre coperto si può impadronirsi della porta A, & della Città, & questo per l'vso dell'artiglierie, con le quali da lontano lieuano le difese, & da presso si entra sotto con la Zappa, e con li cauamenti delle strade sotterranee, & con le ruine delle mine si fa la strada per entrar dentro.

Reuellino & suo officio.

Reuellini & sue imperfettioni.

FORTIFICATIONE FATTA CO' BALVARDI. CAP. V.

EDOPO l'hauere esperimentato i detti torrioni tondi, ritrouarono ancora in parte l'imperfettioni de' primi, cioè, che la parte della sua circonferenza di fuori non era scoperta, ne difesa da' difensori, formando i tiri non solo delle balestre, ma delle artiglierie vn'angolo di fuori, nel quale poteuano stare i nemici coperti, e sicuri. Però conforme alla grandezza del detto an-

FORTEZZA FABRICATA CON MODERNI BALVARDI.

C A P. V I I I.

DALLE imperfettioni conosciute nelle piazze picciole, & dalla debolezza delle sue difese, se n'è cauato quel beneficio, che ne apporta la esperienza, nel ridurre l'opere a quella perfettione, che si desidera, massime in materia delle fortificationi, doue si tratta della salute de gli huomini, & delli Stati de' Prencipi; & per ciò fare habbiamo fino al presente trattato nel presente Libro, delle difese antiche, fatte con quelle imperfettioni, che far si sogliono tutte le cose ne' lor primi principij. E però al presente anderemo mostrãdo quelle difese più sicure, che dalla esperienza sono state conosciute per le più vtili, che far si possano contra le moderne offese, oltre alla facilità, & allo sparagno del danaro nell'effettuare l'opera, e per ciò fare, è necessario, che conforme a siti, & all'offese, si formino esse difese, e non con quella consideratione, che alcuni hanno detto, cioè conforme alle forze del Prencipe, che la può offendere; perche se bene il Prencipe confinante fosse debole di forze, egli si può confederare con altri potenti, & vsare quelle maggiori forze, che vsar si possono, e però conuiene fabricare difese Reali, cioè gran fianchi, per fare grande, & coperte le sue piazze, & similmente cauare con gran larghezza, & con gran profondità la

23, 24 BONAIUTO LORINI, evolution of bastioned front, 1596

25 Rome, Castel S. Angelo, 1557. Three stages of diminishing 'picturesqueness'

Because military architecture evolved, as it were, in a straight line, with each development demonstrably better than the last [23, 24], its practitioners were confident about the quality of what they were doing, a confidence enhanced by their knowledge that they were not just absorbing and modifying the ideas of the ancients but creating new forms in response to a new challenge;[26] they came to trace their ancestry – Girolamo Maggi cited twelve predecessors in 1564,[27] Gabriele Busca seventeen in 1601[28] – in a way no predominantly civil architect could conceivably have done. They were aware, too, that they were part of the intellectual movement which strikes us, perhaps, as the most 'modern' aspect of the Renaissance, the wish to relate specific practical instances to general principles. As one wrote, my aim is to teach 'a universal rule'; another, 'strength resides in form rather than in materials'; yet another, 'the eye of the mind sees more deeply into generalities than does the eye of the body into particulars'.[29] Yet a note of embarrassment can also be heard. The straight line of development was seen to be leading to design principles of an increasingly austere and rigid nature [25]. Moreover, there was no disguising the fact that, whether revetted or not, the new fortifications were basically vast slabs of earth laboriously wheel-barrowed into place to counter force with force. Conscious, then, of having moved far enough from the main body of Vitruvian 'art' values to be in a somewhat exposed position, military architects riposted by stressing the role played in their work by intellect. The classic portico on Galasso Alghisi's title-page [26] advises the reader that the subject should not be approached without adequate intellectual preparation. Below Arithmetic and Geometry on Tensini's [27], the advance of War, with dart and smoking torch, is checked by the winged personification of Intelligence.

A point ignored or glossed over in this literature is that the military architect's design arose in and was frequently modified by committees. It is true that the patron had a say in the planning of a civil structure, that master builders or works overseers might introduce changes for technical

26 Galasso Alghisi, title-page, 1570

reasons, or that, as with Caprarola, or the Farnese Palace, or most dramatically with St Peter's, the design could change as successive architects took over. But when a fortress or a new *enceinte* was planned, the element of compromise was greater. There was necessarily a political presence. Government representatives weighed the consequences of the destruction of property and the forbidding of building or planting on the glacis; quite apart from its drain on local or central treasuries (usually both) the plan of a major fortification had to take account of the loyalties and livelihoods of the local population. A second presence was that of the military. How many men would be required to garrison it? How effective had the proposed features been in past sieges? What strategic support would the new structure lend to armies in the field? Frequently the architect was brought in only when the main decisions as to site and form had been made. And then, almost invariably, changes were demanded in the course of construction, fresh drawings and models called for.

That princes would take a hand in the design of fortifications had been accepted from the start. Filarete describes the architect of his ideal city, Sforzinda, as being allowed to build the walls but, when it came to the citadel, being stopped by his master's firm remark, 'I wish to lay out the fortress in my own fashion.' And the prince proceeds to describe the plan, checking the architect's rough drawings from time to time to make sure that he is following, detail by detail.[30] Florence asked Federigo da Montefeltro to advise in 1472 on the new *rocca* of Volterra. Lorenzo de' Medici intervened in 1488 while Sarzana was being refortified. Sanmicheli himself, in a report on Legnago of 1556, wrote that 'the bastions which have been built with the fullness of knowledge possessed by his excellency Francesco Maria, Duke of Urbino are held by everyone to be the finest and strongest that have yet been constructed.'[31]

This sort of intervention did not rankle. Whether the paymaster or, as in the case of the Duke of Urbino, the adviser to another government,

27 FRANCESCO TENSINI, title-page, 1624

IVS
LA FORTIFICATIONE
GVARDIA DIFESA
ET ESPVGNATIONE
DELLE FORTEZZE
ESPERIMENTATA IN DIVERSE GVERRE
DEL CAVALIERO FRANC.CO TENSINI
DA CREMA
GIA INGEGNERO, CAPITANO, ET LOGOTENENTE
GENERALE DELL' ARTIGLIERIA DEL
DVCA DI BAVIERA, DEL RE DI SPAGNA,
E DELL' IMPERATORE RODOLFO
SECONDO.
ET HORA PERSONAGGIO CONDOTTO DELLA
SER. SIGNORIA DI VENETIA
AL SER.MO PREN.PE ET ECCLE.MO
SENATO VENETO
IN VENETIA.
1624.

the prince represented the patron deferred to in non-military commissions. And the intervention of politicians and bureaucrats in public works was simply a fact of architectural life, then as now. What did bring about a change in the self-image of the military architect was the increasing advisory role played by soldiers and – still more – the proposition that he himself should have had military experience. It was one thing for the architect to move voluntarily into the 'engineering' end of the Vitruvian spectrum, quite another to be transferred right out of it and into that of military skills, even if this meant moving (as a writer in *c.* 1600 put it) into 'the most important and respectable' sector of them.[32]

The shift was, indeed, to lead, slowly but irreversibly, to specialization. It can be charted fairly clearly. Bramante's first advice on a military site had been turned down in 1493 by Lodovico Sforza, Duke of Milan, who ordered his replacement by someone 'better qualified in matters appertaining to war'.[33] Stronger evidence comes with an early comment on Michelangelo's work on the defences of Florence in 1529: 'it is the role of the architect to draw up the plans and the model of fortifications according to the site. . . . But an understanding of whence they will be attacked and how defended, and what will be the effectiveness of flanks and embrasures is not the business of the architect but of an experienced, worthy and good soldier who has been not just the conceiver but the defender of fortresses. If he [Michelangelo] was wanting in this respect, it was the fault of those who did not associate such men with him.'[34]

Among the soldiers then attacking Florence was Francesco de' Marchi. Later he became an engineer – he designed a diving-bell in which he made two long descents into the Lake of Nemi to study the Roman vessels lying on its bed – and a respected military architect. Faithful to the Vitruvian spectrum, however, he wrote a treatise on civil architecture, and it was he who in 1558 won the competition for the design of Margaret of Austria's palace in Piacenza. But his treatise on fortification,[35] written *c.* 1550, reveals a deep unease about his role. While stressing the importance of a preliminary study of 'the good Marco Vitruvio', praising the dignity of architecture and producing an impressive battery of references to the ancients, he none the less claims to write as a soldier for soldiers, aiming to bring war into touch with architecture rather than vice versa.

In a treatise written shortly afterwards by Belluzzi, then chief military engineer to Duke Cosimo I, the author agreed with Michelangelo's critic that fortification needed the collaboration of two men, one gifted conceptually, the other with more practical gifts. But his contention was that both should be professional soldiers.[36] In 1570 Alghisi took his stand on tradition, warning his readers against 'certain persecutors of the *virtuosi* who, under cover of their reputation as soldiers, seek to usurp the role in military affairs which necessarily belongs to architects.'[37] Scamozzi, too, reaffirmed the Vitruvian credo of architectural omnicompetence. Like street-plans, churches and palaces, walls were the architect's business. Soldiers might know about attack and defence; this he admitted, but just as prelates did not design their own churches nor princes their palaces, the military should not claim to be able to plan and execute fortifications.[38]

This was by then a rearguard action. The burst of new or modified fortifications that strained the budget of every Italian government in the sixteenth century, called for far more military engineers than could be found among those who had established a reputation for designing civil structures. De' Marchi gave a two-page list of successful sieges to prove his point that constant experiment and rebuilding was necessary. It was made more forcefully by Captain Giovanni da Torino who, when told by Siena to defend Montalcino in 1552, replied that unless the town's walls were modernized he would refuse 'even if he was ordered to do so by Christ in person'.[39]

From the 1520s the frequent need for the hasty adaptation of walls led the authors of manuals written for soldiers to provide instruction in the elements of fortification.[40] The needs of war itself led to the creation of something like an apprenticeship and a career structure for this particular branch of architectural practice. The soldier with an eye for existing fortifications and a smattering of information from books, numerate enough to learn elementary surveying and alert to talk to gunners and the veterans of sieges and assaults, became increasingly likely to be deputed to supervise defence works. In 1501 Basilio dalla Scola, hitherto a soldier and artillerist, displayed in Venice a wooden model of a fortress 'which incorporated what is being done in France, Italy . . ., Germany and elsewhere'. Thus began a career as a military architect, first for Venice, then in Germany and finally, in 1520, in Rhodes.[41] By 1600, out of Venice's permanent staff of nine military engineers, eight had started as soldiers. None performed civilian tasks more demanding than the design of barracks and munition stores, though one of them, Lorini, and a later recruit, Tensini, became highly literate and respected spokesmen for what was becoming a specialized profession.

This generalization, however, needs qualification. While some men started as soldiers and ended – as did Tensini – as military engineers, and others, like Lorini, began as architects anxious to develop their understanding of fortifications in the context of war and, receiving no civil commissions on their travels outside Italy, ended by having specialization forced upon them, the division between civil and military architecture was not mandatory even in the second half of the sixteenth century. In 1584, for instance, the Duke of Savoy signed a contract appointing 'Captain Ascanio Vitozzi of Orvieto as our Engineer and Architect'. Vitozzi, who had served at Lepanto and fought in Hungary, was not unusual in being employed now on a fortress, now on an urban planning development, now on a church; among his colleagues in Savoy was Busca, son of a gunfounder and employed in the first instance as an artillerist, and the ex-soldier, Giacomo Soldati.[42] Like Vitozzi, they too were expected to be able to turn their hands to the design of street decorations for pageants and to civilian structures; and, though none of these men had the genius of their contemporary Buontalenti, Soldati was credited with the addition of a new architectural order, the 'Harmonic', to the Vitruvian repertory of Doric, Ionian and the rest.[43]

There remained a place for the gifted amateur, like Giovanni de' Medici, a *virtuoso* whose designs for the Belvedere fortress and the Cappella dei Principi in S. Lorenzo were treated with equal seriousness. And it was still possible to be invited to design fortifications without practical experience of any kind. Even before the spread of printed treatises on fortification, military architects had been plagued by the suggestions of armchair pundits. They had irritated Sanmicheli, and when the principles of fortification came to be taught in university cities, as by Galileo at Padua from 1592, the opportunities for irritation were enhanced. 'This craft', Tomaso de Venetia (who had begun as a soldier) was moved to say, 'is not to be learned in Bologna or Perugia or Padua nor out of books, but in action.'[44] Yet that there was a form of purely bookish 'special entry' into the profession emerges from the career of Girolamo Maggi, a classical scholar who turned himself into a fortifications expert and paid for the transformation with his life when the Turks took Famagosta in 1571, and from that of the Protestant theologian Jacopo Aconcio. At risk in Italy for his religious views, 'my mind', he wrote, 'was vexed with plans to flee whither I might freely profess the Gospel, and I thought it possible that if I might learn this art it would thereafter give me a living. So whenever I had a chance I carefully questioned everyone about what they had tried to do, and what they admired or condemned in every fortress.' So successful was his questioning of soldiers and engineers that he was brought to England as an expert by Sir William Cecil and played a part in the design of the greatest English military project of the period, the fortifications at Berwick.[45]

Qualifications apart, however, there was a significant shift in practice and values between the middle of the Quattrocento and the middle of the Cinquecento. In the former, the notion of military architecture assumed that *disegno* was the prompting talent of its practitioners, and that its exponents were at least touched by the hem of Vitruvian respectability. In the latter, the ability to learn from campaigning experience became the index of talent, and shelter beneath Vitruvius' mantle became a last, and self-conscious, resort.

We must now ask: did this shift affect the way in which fortifications were appraised from an aesthetic (or, at least, non-utilitarian) point of view, and, if so, does this knowledge help us to clarify our own reaction to them?

The problem here is that Renaissance man, with all his reputation for possessing a tingling response to any challenge to his senses, was generally laconic when faced by bricks and mortar. Ornament provoked a richer vocabulary of appreciation than did structure. But because of its vulnerability to shot, ornament came to be suppressed. 'Fortresses need no architects' – this was one of Belluzzi's most emphatic points – 'because they need no cornices or architraves or swags of flowers or other carved work which the cannon would send up in smoke; they need good flanks.'[46] Antonio da San Gallo's suggestion that Pope Paul III should ignore Michelangelo's plans for protecting the Borgo because 'his profession was sculpture and painting, and not fortification'[47] pointed in the same direction. In fact the formula Machiavelli used in his *Art of War*: 'where strength is necessary no account is taken of beauty', might seem to settle the contemporary viewpoint, were it not that he was commenting not on fortifications but on the spokes of a gun-carriage. As it is, we must briefly take a closer look.

Alberti had agreed that 'delicate cornices and incrustations are not proper for the walls of a town'. All the same, 'beauty', he claimed, 'will have such an effect upon an enraged enemy that it will disarm his anger . . . insomuch that I will be bold to say, there can be no greater security . . . than beauty and dignity'. What he had in mind was

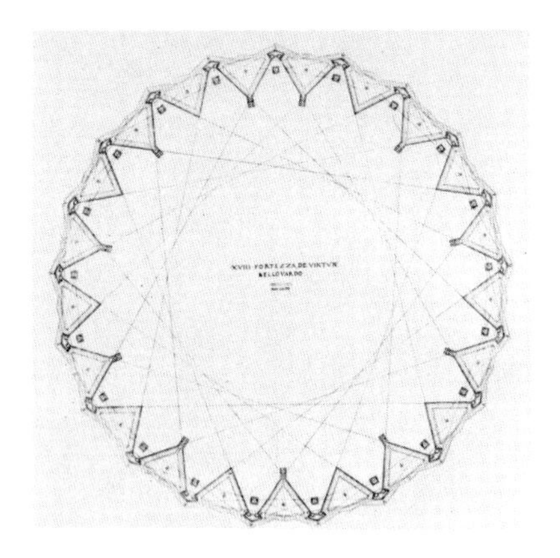

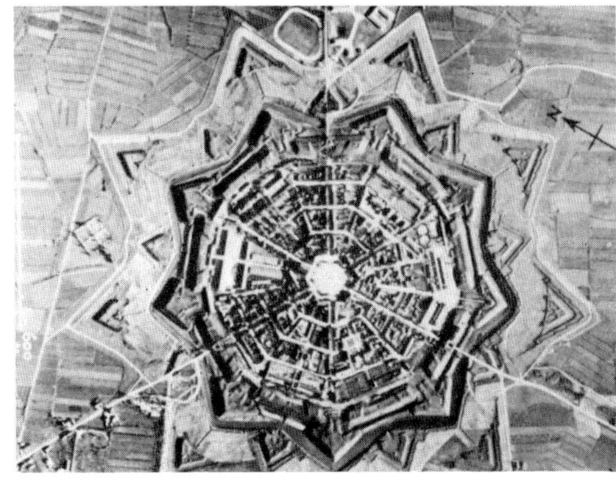

28 GALASSO ALGHISI, ideal *enceinte* of 21 bastions
29 GIULIO SAVORGNAN and others, Palma (now Palmanova), begun 1593

explained elsewhere when he wrote that a fortress 'ought to look fierce, terrible, rugged, dangerous and unconquerable'.[48] The words were echoed a century later by Pietro Cataneo: a citadel must look 'rugged, proud, threatening'.[49]

These last words are, of course, associative, not critical. And though they create a powerful image of the over-all impression fortifications could give, their applicability dwindled as these sank lower and lower (to present an ever-shrinking target) until the designer's ideal was reached and, apart from their earthen parapets, they became invisible.

With the suppression first of ornament and then of outline, the source of aesthetic response became the spare patterns of geometry [28]. We must not underestimate the pleasure these could give. Raphael was flattering a man he greatly admired when he identified Bramante with Euclid in *The School of Athens*. That dignity, certainty and beauty were inherent in geometrical forms was axiomatic throughout the Renaissance. But the appeal was necessarily limited. These harmonies could be sensed, the whole could be imagined from the part. But while anyone could respond to a proud and threatening silhouette, few could react to the gigantic snowflake of Palma even from its ramparts until,

30 BRAMANTE (?completed by MICHELANGELO), *mastio* of fortress at Civitavecchia, from 1508
31 ANTONIO DA SAN GALLO THE YOUNGER, *mastio* of Fortezza da Basso, Florence, begun 1534

long afterwards, men took to the air [29]. And the few who could have reacted did not voice their feelings.

Palma is an unusual, an extreme case, and lies at the limit of our period.[50] But even in the mid Cinquecento it was acknowledged that fortifications as a whole could impart only a general sensation of power while the spectator's eye searched for an ornamentation that was but grudgingly accorded. 'This sort of massive and military architecture', warned Maggi in 1564, 'requires little ornament, the architect needing to have an eye only for the robustness and the brave impression of the work. All the same, it seems to many that if only a moderate expense is incurred some ornamentation may be added so long as it appears impressive rather than simply pleasant to the eye [30], such as footings [at the base of the scarp], cordons with carved strips below them, and ashlar finishing, rusticated, though not too deeply, at the corners of the bastions.'[51]

Apart from an occasional decorative feature like the masonry

32 GIULIANO DA SAN GALLO, fortress at Poggio Imperiale, from 1488
33 ANTONIO DA SAN GALLO THE ELDER (with GIULIANO), Civitacastellana, *rocca*, begun 1494

rendering of the Medici *palle* and diamonds on the Fortezza da Basso [31] in Florence (pronounced by Vasari to be 'very rich and varied and most beautiful to look at') and coats of arms, Maggi was accurately describing the austerity that followed the transitional period, the late fourteenth and early fifteenth centuries, when the old style and the new consorted in a happy combination of severity and display [32, 33]. And his reference to expense rings true. Even during the transitional period governments were prepared to pay for utility but not for all the ornamentation the builders wanted. While Sarzana's fortifications were being renewed in 1489 the Florentine governor was told: 'we have seen the drawing of the main tower . . . and have resolved to set ornament aside and concentrate on utility and speed . . . so keep the scarp of the tower simple, without footings or the use of cut stone'.[52]

The only feature which consistently defied the demands of utility and speed – indeed, the open acknowledgment that brick and stone were primarily a protective cladding[53] – was the gate; and the compression of the architect's love of ornament into this small focus produced works that combined, as the treatise-writers said they must, ornament with utility and strength [34]. Serlio recommended a mixture of the Tuscan and Rustic orders, and his lions' heads were not only symbols of strength but actually useful, as their mouths were pierced for muskets [35]. Scamozzi was to warn against classicizing a fortress's gate into a simulated triumphal arch whose more delicate features would be knocked off and become 'trophies of the enemy'.[54]

The interest here is that in no other context in Scamozzi's long discussion of fortifications did he imply the possibility of judging them as works of art. And, with the striking nineteenth-century exception of the Dominican Alberto Guglielmotti,[55] his example has been followed until comparatively recently. The situation now – to summarize crudely – is this. What Carlo Promis referred to as long ago as 1863 as 'that enormous fact: the pentagonal bastion'[56] has become the object of considerable historical study, although this is still largely unevaluative.

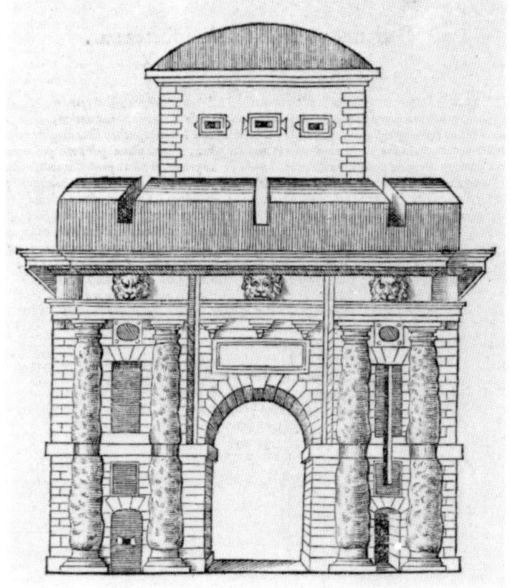

34 Sanmicheli, Verona, Porta Palio, begun *c.* 1548

35 SEBASTIANO SERLIO, fortified gate, published 1584

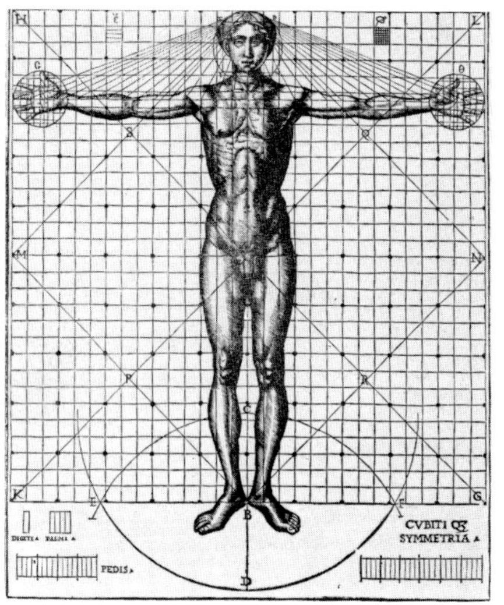

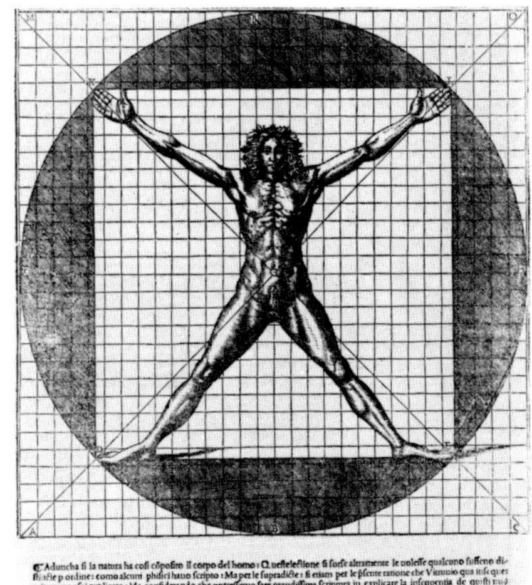

36 Man the measure; C. Cesariano's edition of Vitruvius, 1521

37 Man the origin of circle and square, Cesariano

However, students of those 'art' architects who designed fortifications as well as civil buildings are at last attempting to absorb military architecture into an over-all critical appraisal. Finally, Renaissance fortification is being re-examined in the light of three conceptual fashions: anthropomorphology, symbolism and urban planning.

Of these, the first two ask whether there were notions abroad, other than technological ones, which could have affected the planning of fortifications as the revolution settled into its stride. With the anthropomorphic approach we return to Vitruvius, this time to those powerfully evocative figures the *homo ad circulum* and the *homo ad quadratum* [36, 37]. Vitruvius made two points; that the elements of the column derived from the measurements – head, body, legs, feet – of the human body, and that the body, the source of the circle and the square, was also the exemplar of the harmony and proportion[57] to be observed in all correct building. Alberti allowed that the first contention was 'not improbable'. Filarete wrote that 'proportions, qualities . . . the square

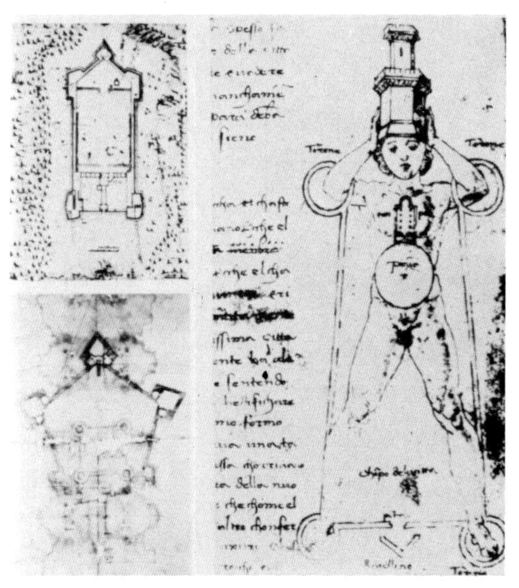

and every other measure is derived from man'. And he began what was to become a long series of anthropomorphic comparisons. Thus the patron begets a plan upon the architect; this matures in his mind 'for seven to nine months' after which he is delivered of a wooden model. Or, again, he speaks of a building sickening and dying like a man unless it receives medical attention in the form of regular maintenance.[58] Later, in the literature of fortification, and, indeed, in common parlance, bastions were compared to arms, their batteries to eyes, the lobed projections which protected them were called 'ears', 'shoulders', 'snouts', even – Pietro Cataneo put this down to the influence of the military – 'testicles'.

But this is very different from saying that military engineers planned their works to *look* like the human body or parts of it. In his very extensive comments on the passage which evoked these illustrations Cesariano did not suggest this, nor did any other Vitruvian commentator. When Michelangelo wrote that 'there is no question that architectural members reflect the members of man'[59] or Vasari that a palace 'must represent the body of a man in the whole and similarly in

38 Francesco di Giorgio, 'fortress man', with (top left) Poggio Imperiale
39 G. B. Cairati, Fort Jesus, Mombasa, begun 1593

40 Francesco di Giorgio, fortress design, *c.* 1490

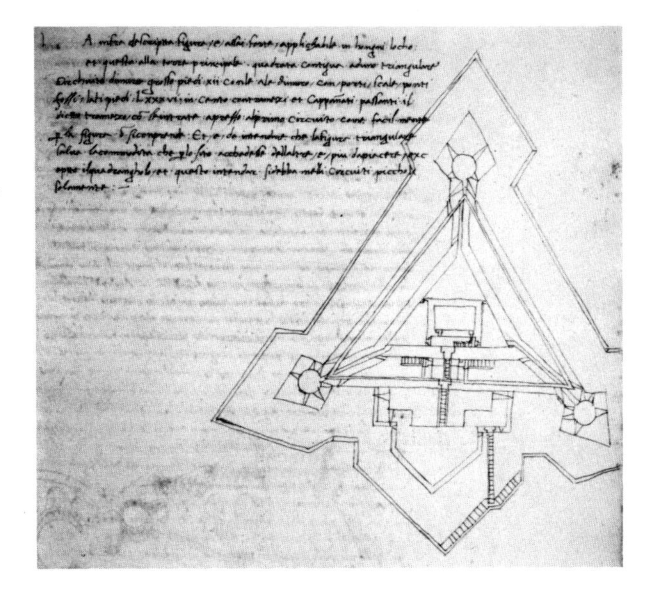

the parts' – including those that drain away superfluities, filth and smells[60] – they were talking not about likeness but function or proportion; as was Scamozzi when he declared that a well-designed fortress 'should have all its parts disposed according to their function just as nature, the true teacher of things, has formed and apportioned the members of the human body'.[61]

Yet largely on the basis of a drawing in one manuscript of Francesco di Giorgio's treatise, and its resemblance to the contemporary layout of Poggio Imperiale [38], it has been claimed that fortresses were, on occasion at least, designed to correspond literally to the dimensions of the human body. By one author we are even invited to see the tower-gate-tower complex at Poggio in terms of 'the legs . . . defending the genital organs by flanking them', and to understand this in terms of the phallic emphasis of primitive pictograms which show how deeply imprinted in the human mind is the instinct to create forms resembling the human body.[62] Fort Jesus, in Mombasa [39], is another fortress whose design has been explained in anthropomorphic terms.[63] Not only is the idea inherently unlikely, but there is not a shred of evidence for it: none of the scores of plans designed by Francesco di Giorgio for the same treatise [40], for instance, does anything but support his contention in the text that the basis of the plan should be the rhomb and other angular forms.[64] It is true that the cruciform church could be seen as a reference to Christ on the cross; Pietro Cataneo recommended that the principal church in a newly planned city should be designed 'in the similitude of a well-proportioned human body',[65] but while the shape of a church could respond to a metaphysical advocacy of cross (or circle) without damage to its function, that of a military work could not. The anthropomorphic approach leads to mere dottiness. Its interest resides solely in the evidence it provides of a desire to add a non-engineering element to the reappraisal of Renaissance fortifications.

This is also the chief interest of the approach that stresses the symbolism of fortifications. Walls were, of course, powerful symbols of security and sovereignty, as is shown by Vasari's fresco in the Palazzo Vecchio [41] which identifies the founding of Florence both with the furrow, signifying the act of possession, and the protective – and faithfully Vitruvian – towers. The *rocca* or citadel was consciously seen as a symbol of authority, the badge of princely or foreign domination, and was discussed in these terms by architects, politicians and populace alike. When the Medici built the Fortezza da Basso athwart the old republican city wall, it was hailed as 'a yoke for their adversaries'.

Certainly, it is important to understand the symbolic overtones of fortifications, as part of their significance to contemporaries; but it is a far cry from this to the suggestion that symbolism affected their design. It has been proposed, for instance, that the *retardataire* features [1] of the transition period – towers, false machicolation and the like – and, more generally, the tendency to repair rather than modernize, were due to a cherishing of the symbolic implications of medieval structures.[66] Apart from a single expression of regret for the slighting of some of the towers of Florence during preparations for the siege of 1529, there is no evidence for this assertion.[67] Moreover, traditionalism is not to be identified with

41 GIORGIO VASARI, detail from fresco *The Foundation of Florence*; Florence, Palazzo Vecchio, Salone del Cinquecento

symbolism; nor is nostalgia, nor is the desire to retain opportunities for complexity or display. These were the motives, qualifying technological logic, that conditioned the appearance of transitional works, just as sloth, stinginess and a lack of urgency are better explanations of a reluctance to modernize.

The search for symbolic explanations of form can also lead to patent absurdity. Thus a five-pointed star was highly commended for the design of sixteenth-century forts and citadels [42, 43] as being the cheapest and most practical way of enclosing a space which could be defended by a small garrison while maintaining a desirable relationship between the length of a bastion's flank and its adjacent curtain wall. It has recently been suggested, however, that the chief influence was the significance of the star-shaped astrological diagram [44], and 'the resulting desire to follow such a model for magical reasons, or as homage to the mystical Platonic or Pythagorean "perfection" of the pentagram'.[68] It is surely unlikely that symbolism had anything to do

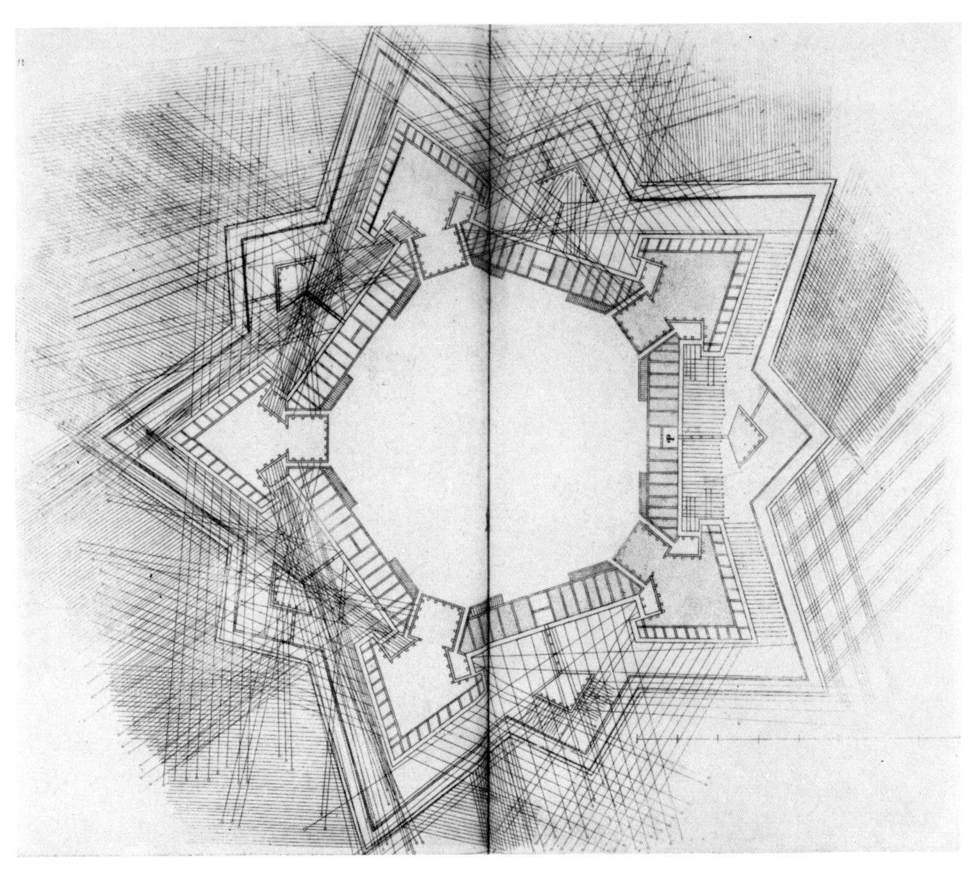

42 FRANCESCO DE' MARCHI, design for pentagonal fort with ravelins, *c.* 1545

with a form found to be practical well into the nineteenth century [45]. This approach is, all the same, further evidence of a renewed interest in Renaissance fortifications, a flinching from their 'engineering' aspect – and, indeed, of a general uncertainty about the criteria by which they should be judged. Thus the author of the latest study of Bramante deals confidently with his civic and ecclesiastical buildings, but, faced with the *rocca* at Civitavecchia, feels bound to conjecture that the design incorporates the symbolic crossed keys and triple crown and may contain anthropomorphic or magical overtones.[69]

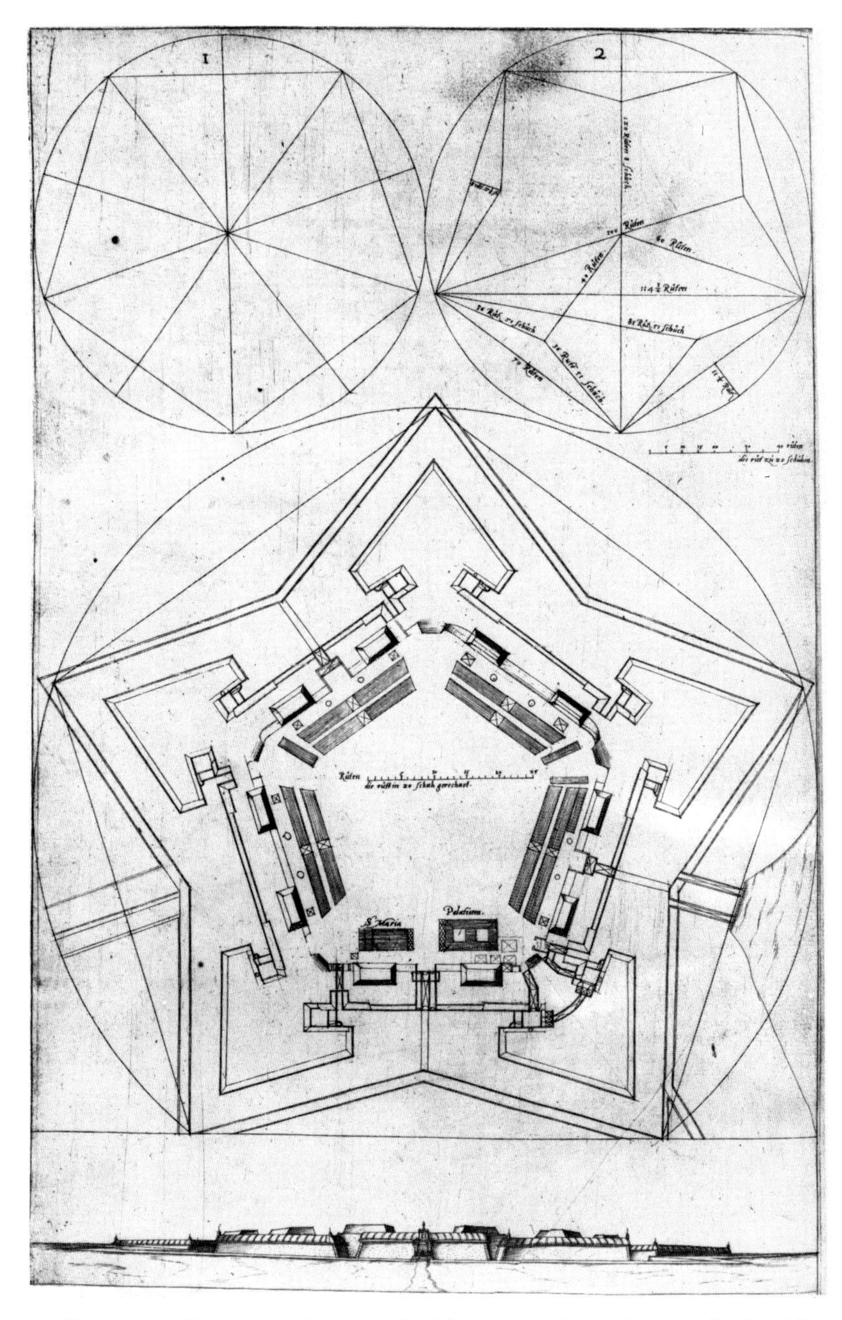

43 FRANCESCO PACIOTTO, Antwerp citadel, 1567–9, plan and analysis by Daniel Speckle, 1589

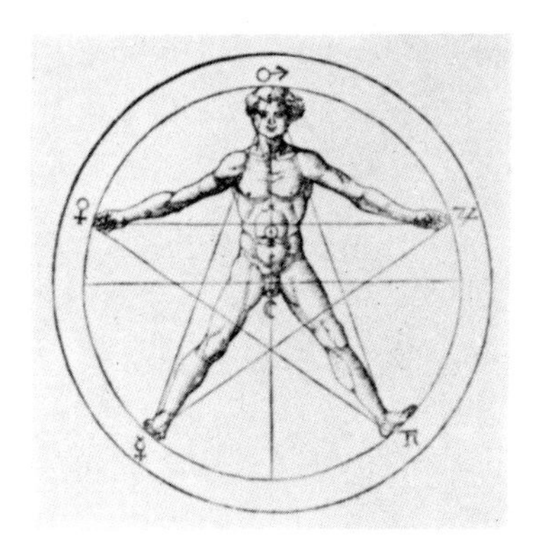

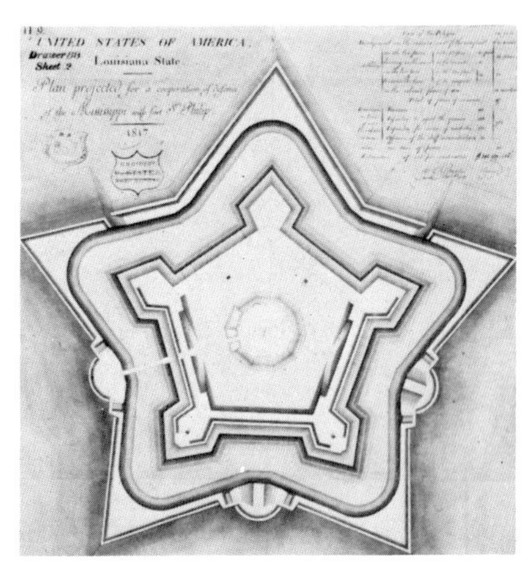

44 Pentagram from Henricus Cornelius Agrippa, *De occulta philosophia*, 1533
45 Fort on Mississippi to guard New Orleans, plan, 1817

46 FRANCESCO PACIOTTO and others, Lucca *enceinte*, from 1561

47 Ferrara. Herculanean Addition, from 1492, northern half

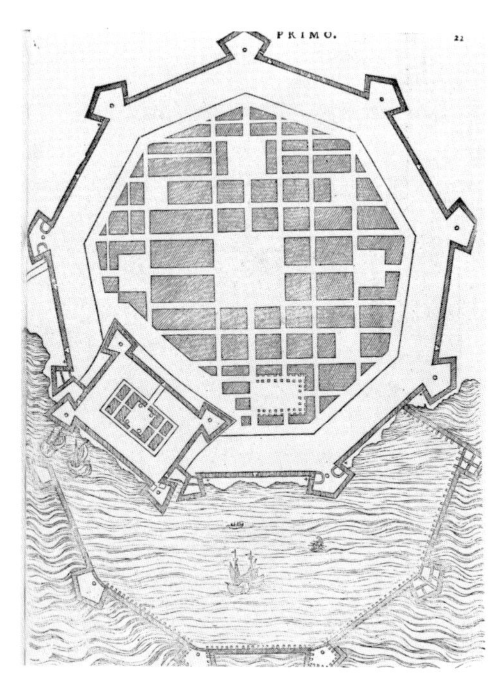

48 Pietro Cataneo, ideal grid town plan, 1554

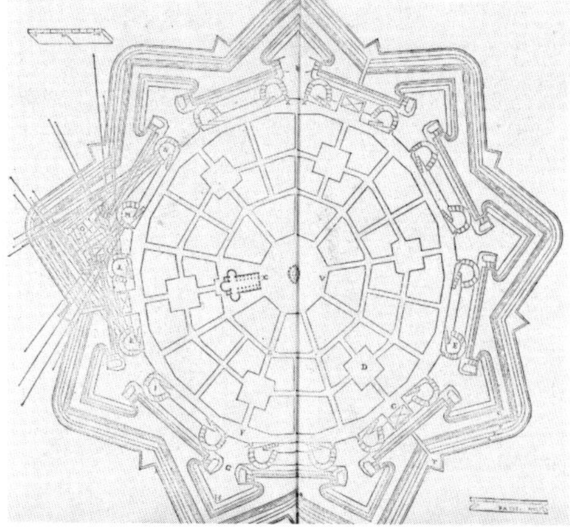

49 Bonaiuto Lorini, ideal radial town plan, 1596

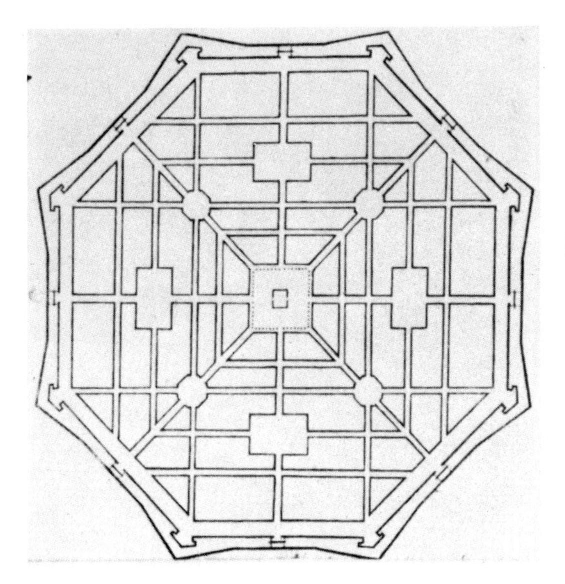

50 GIORGIO VASARI THE YOUNGER, combination grid and radial plan, 1570

In addition to these 'cultural' approaches, the post-war preoccupation with urbanism has led to an interest in fortifications; study of the inside of Renaissance cities, both ideal and actual, leading to a closer look at the outside, the walls [46, 47]. Vitruvius started with the walls and then, as he said, 'the next step is the apportionment of house lots and the laying out of streets.' And his Renaissance disciples followed him. 'The most important matter in the whole of architecture', as Cataneo put it, 'apart from the walls, is the proper division and distribution of the streets, the *piazze* and the *pomerio*' (the open space between the walls and the urban fabric). And as it was above all in the books dealing entirely, or (as in his case) to an important degree, with fortifications, that ideal cities were illustrated and discussed, and as the study of town-planning, especially the planning of ideal towns, is held to be closer to art than to engineering, the study of fortifications has acquired, by association, an aesthetic respectability. But the association is, alas, not at all close. In Renaissance discussions of the ideal town there is some talk about the tactical importance of a central *piazza*, about the pros and cons of radial versus grid-pattern streets from the point of view of blocking an enemy advance or getting more defenders to a breach, whether streets should run to the throats of bastions or to the centre of stretches of curtain wall [48–50]. But more commonly the association is trivial, as when Scamozzi recommends avoiding paving-stones lest the enemy hear the tramp of feet and the clatter of hooves and wheels; or irrelevant – the influence of Vitruvius' recommendation that streets should be oriented in terms of the prevailing winds, not of war [51, 52]; or the association is simply omitted from lack of interest or, more frequently, because of Cataneo's *pomerio*. This, too, was a Vitruvian concept. It was applied in actual new or extended towns to allow space for troop assemblies [53], for the building of inner defences to contain a breach [54], or simply for recreation. And it blurred the need for the street-plan to correspond closely to that of the defences.

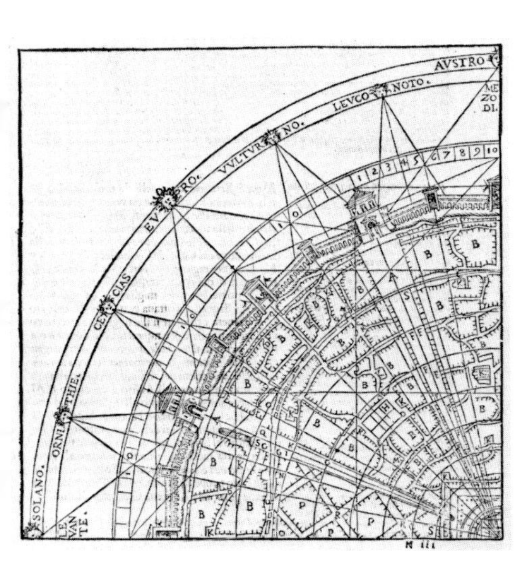

51 Wind rose and town plan, G. Caporali's translation of Vitruvius, 1536
52 GIROLAMO MAGGI, wind rose and street plan, 1564

53 (overleaf) FRANCESCO DE' MARCHI, octagonal ideal town plan (with perspective urban blocks) showing *pomerio* ▷

Pomerio
Fosso
Fosso
Cap.no franc. de Marchi inventore

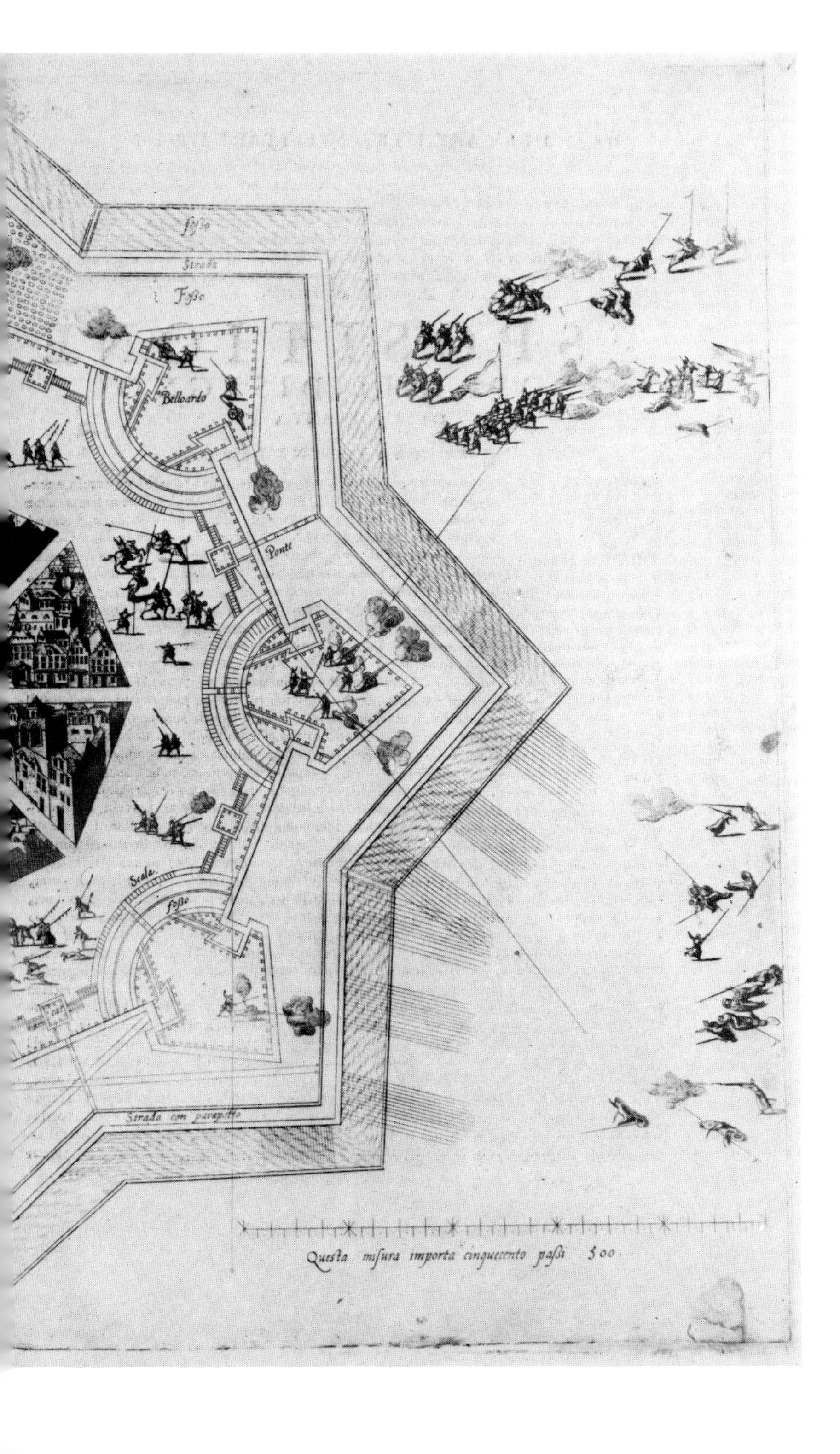
fosso
Strada
Fosso
Belloardo
Ponte
Scala
fosso
Strada con parapetto
Questa misura importa cinquecento passi 500.

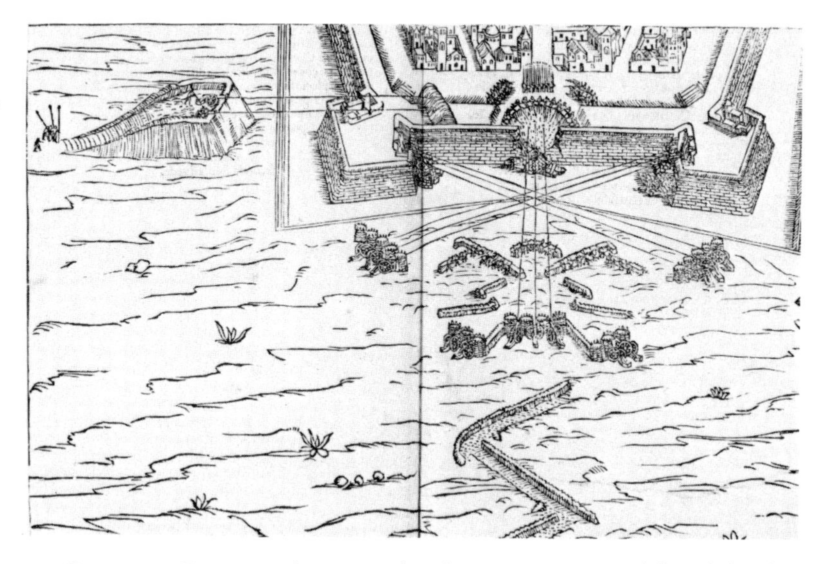

54 GIROLAMO CATANEO, siege scene, showing emergency inner defence behind breach

In any case, none of the significant examples of Renaissance urban expansion shows a textbook fit between inside and outside. Either, as at Ferrara, Guastalla or Sabbioneta, enlargement had to take account of existing buildings, or, as at Civitavecchia or Livorno, an 'ideal' circuit of defences had to wait for a larger population to edge towards it in a gradual, *ad hoc* fashion. Of the three entirely new foundations, Poggio Imperiale and Terra del Sole [56] did not attract enough settlement to join streets to walls, and Palma's street-plan [55], which was not the work of its military designers, has led to the judgment that 'Palma the fortress was emasculated in a futile attempt to create Palma the city'.[70]

But the study of historic cities has two faces. If the one which looks from the centre towards the walls has done little more than call attention to them, the one which looks at the townscape from the viewpoint of the countryside has awakened a visual alertness to the architectonic qualities of fortifications, and a novel empathy with those who passed in and out of them [57, 58].

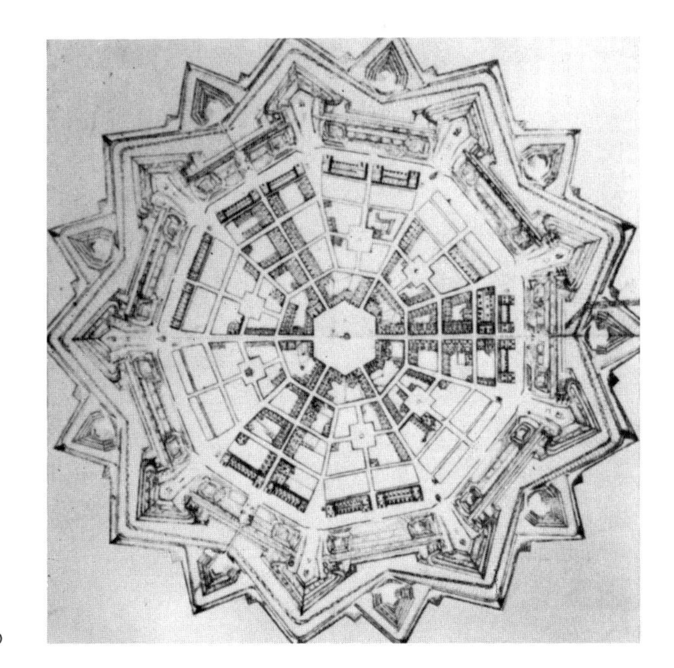

55 Palma, plan, *c.* 1695

56 Terra del Sole, plan *c.* 1490

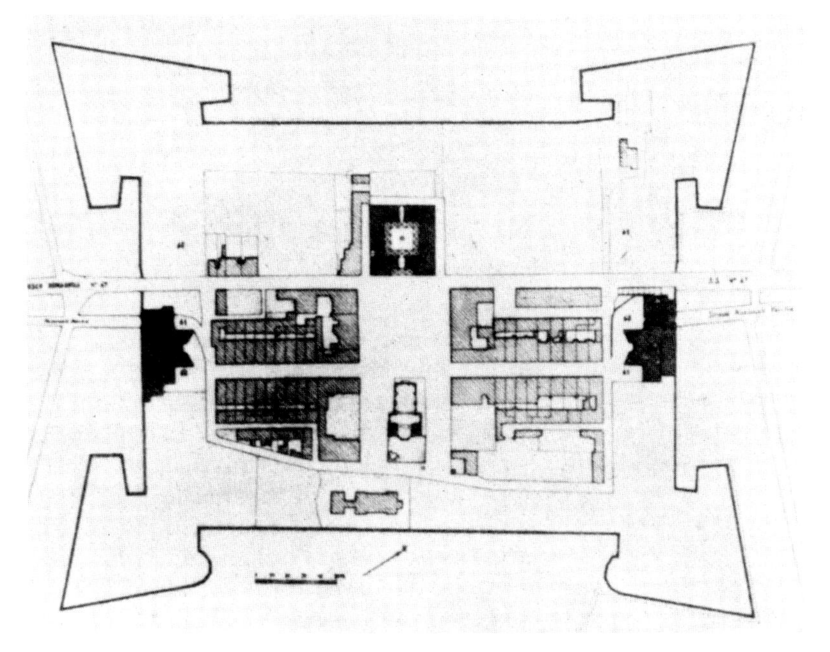

57 Bergamo, upper town, *enceinte*, 1561–88

58 GABRIELE BUSCA, *enceinte* and outworks, 1601

59 MICHELANGELO, drawing of bastion for Florence, ?1526

This alertness has been further stimulated by art historians who have used fortifications as a point of departure for looking at architecture rather than as an irrelevant technological cul-de-sac. It is widely accepted that the dynamism of Michelangelo's fortification drawings [59] helped him to break up 'the static figures and proportions of the Quattrocentro', to attain a new plastic freedom.[71] More recently, the enhanced plasticity and expressiveness of Leonardo's later drawings has been attributed to his interest in fortifications and fire patterns [8].[72] There have also been suggestions that work on fortifications nourished the austerity needed to monumentalize and control the Quattrocento enthusiasm for classical motifs, that because defence works had to remain relatively immune to changes in style they helped to steady the extremer consequences of Mannerist freedom: permitting the 'return to Michelozzo' of Buontalenti's severely rational villas, in the same way that *émigré* Italian military architects like Paciotto may have influenced the return to the *estilo desornamentado* in Spain.

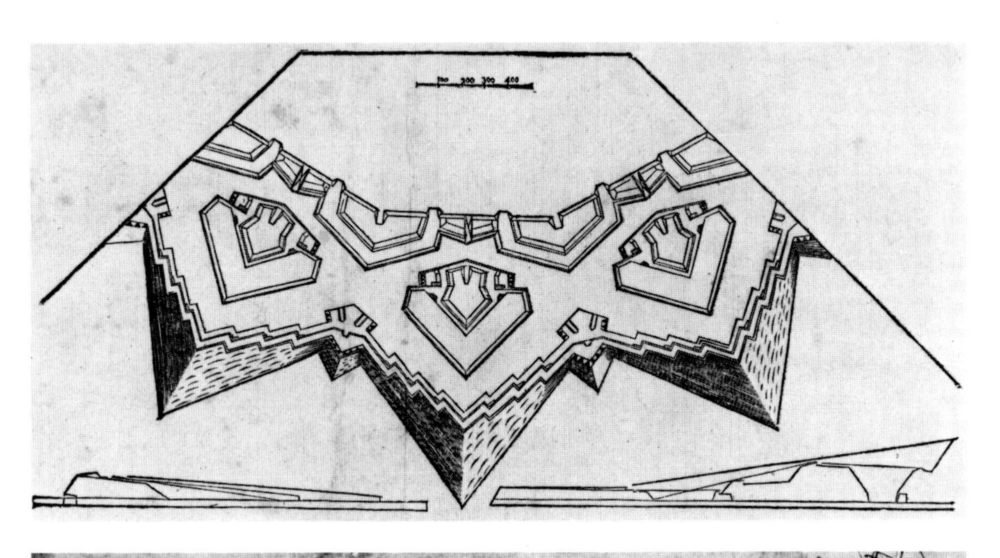
100 200 300 400

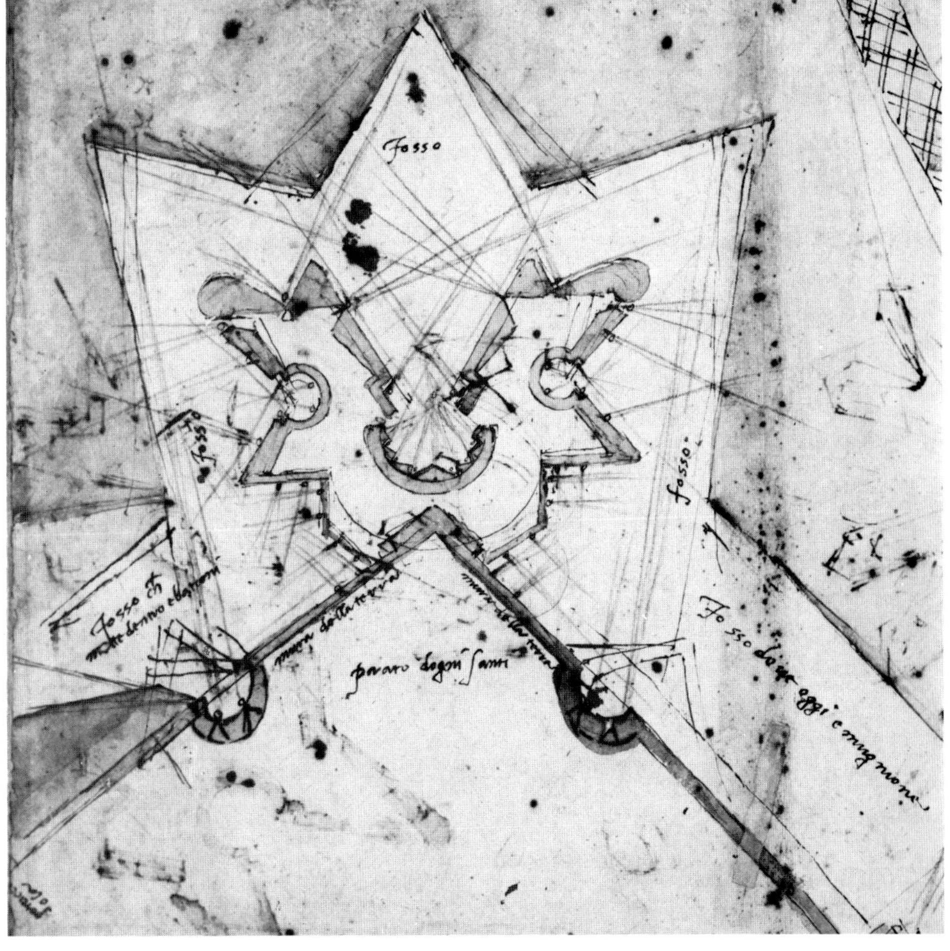
Fosso
Fosso
fosso
muro della terra
prato dogni Santi

To some extent, then, the study of Renaissance fortification is opening out, arousing a new interest. The interest is overdue. (I doubt whether S. Andrea would be faced with collapse had it been a church or palace of comparable quality.) How, in conclusion, can that interest be extended?

Surely by our visiting fortifications (as Renaissance travellers did) with something of the interest and spirit of judgment we bring to civil and ecclesiastical structures. We no longer flinch from finding pleasure in works where function predominates. We can take pleasure in grain stores and cooling towers, admire, indeed, shapes determined by the mindless flow of air in a wind tunnel. Almost automatically we apply the standards of art to the products of engineering. And we cannot be immune to the human significance of fortifications as an architectural commentary on changing conditions of security and terror. But interest can only be intense if it is accompanied by discrimination. There are fortresses whose lean energy can exhilarate [61]; others are as dull as the

60 Bastion at Peschiera del Lago

61 GIULIANO DA SAN GALLO, bastion at Borgo San Sepolcro, 1502–5

ditchwater that surrounds them [60]. Why is this? I have cautiously left myself no time to answer the question. It is a matter of the relationship of the building to its terrain, of the parts to the mass; the way in which space is sliced into by bastions, cradled in their flanks; gun ports and embrasures can be judged as fenestration can be; the appropriateness of a wall's height and impression of solidity to the shafts, ducts and countermine corridors within it can be sensed and appraised; gates can be valid expressions of the power inherent in the system as a whole or mere façadism. In a word, the question 'art or engineering' can be asked, and can be answered; and until it is, some of the Renaissance's finest works will continue to be used as dumps and pulled apart by waves or weeds.

NOTES

1 Bruno Zevi, *Biagio Rossetti*... (Turin, 1960) 150, complains that 'the integration of so-called "military architecture" into the history of architecture as it really should be understood, is as yet an unsolved problem'. Lionello Puppi, *Michele Sanmicheli*... (Padua, 1971), sees the appreciation of fortifications as hampered by the opposition between the 'two cultures', humanist and scientific.

2 Franco Buselli, *Documenti sulla edificazione della fortezza di Sarzana* [and Sarzanello], *1487–1492* (Florence, 1970) 70.

3 Illus. in P. Sanpaolesi, *Brunelleschi* (Milan, 1962). His fortifications at Vicopisano were hailed as 'whatever one could desire for self-defence and for attacking anyone who might set about them' by experienced *condottieri*. Antonio Manetti, *The Life of Brunelleschi*, ed. H. Saalman (Penn. State U., 1970) 120.

4 For illustrations see J.R. Hale, 'The development of the bastion; an Italian chronology', *Europe in the Late Middle Ages*, ed. J.R. Hale, R. Highfield and B. Smalley (London, 1965).

5 Though his drawings of fortifications (8 and 59) are usually associated with this appointment, their chronology is not firmly established.

6 'Life of Orcagna'.

7 Cellini, emphasizing the casual way in which architects were prepared, wrote that there were even 'some without training in *disegno* who, feeling drawn to this worthy art of architecture, began to practise it and had the good fortune to be employed by great lords.' 'Discorso dell'architettura', *Opere* (Milan, 1811) iii, 246.

8 Inventory printed by P. Sanpaolesi in *Palladio* (1951) 44 seq.

9 *De re aedificatoria* (completed *c.* 1452) tr. J. Leoni (London, 1955) 207.

10 *I quattro primi libri di architettura* (Venice, 1554) 1 r–v.

11 Puppi, op. cit., 22–3.

12 Richard A. Goldthwaite, 'The building of the Strozzi palace . . .', *Studies in Medieval and Renaissance History* (1973) 134.

13 G. Lanteri, *Due dialoghi . . . del modo di disegnare le piante delle fortezze secondo Euclide* (Venice, 1557) 45.

14 G. Alghisi, *Delle fortificationi* (Venice, 1570) 406.

15 F.D. Prager and G. Scaglia, *Brunelleschi: Studies of his Technology and Inventions* (London, 1970) 128.

16 'Life of Cecca'.

17 Tr. M.H. Morgan (London, 1960) 3 and 16.

18 G. Baldwin Brown, intro. to *Vasari on Technique* (New York, 1960) 25n.

19 Giano Bigazzini, v. *Dizionario biografico degli italiani.*

20 Tr. cit., 96.

21 M. Dezzi Bardeschi, 'Le rocche di Francesco di Giorgio nel ducato di Urbino', *Castellum* (8, 1968) 97–140.

22 W.B. Dinsmoor, 'The literary remains of Sebastiano Serlio', *Art Bulletin* (1942) 55–91, 115–159.

23 *La città* . . ., ed. M. Fossi (Rome, 1970).

24 *La città ideale*, ed. Virginia Stefanelli (Rome, 1970) 64.
25 'Francesco Paciotto, architect', *Essays in Memory of Karl Lehmann* (New York, 1964) 178.
26 E.g. G.B. Zanchi, *Del modo di fortificar le città* (Venice, 1560) 59, and Alghisi, op. cit., dedication.
27 *Della fortificatione* . . . (Venice, 1564) lib. 1, c. xi.
28 *Della architettura militare* (Milan, 1601) 123–4.
29 Zanchi, op. cit., 10–11; Maggi, op. cit., 21r; N. Tartaglia, *Quesiti et inventioni* (Venice, 1538) quo. F.L. Taylor, *The Art of War in Italy, 1494–1529* (Cambridge, 1921) 165.
30 *Treatise on Architecture*, tr. John R. Spencer (London, 1965) i, 65 seq.
31 Archivio di Stato, Venice. Provveditori alle Fortezze 65, i, n.p.
32 Biblioteca Nazionale, Florence, Ms. XIX, 142 (2) f. 1r.
33 A. Bruschi, *Bramante architetto* (Bari, 1969) xxx.
34 Quo. P. Barocchi, ed., Vasari *Vita di Michelangelo* (5 vols., Milan, 1962) iii, 918.
35 *Della architettura militare* . . . (Brescia, 1599).
36 *Nuova invenzione di fabbricar fortezze* (publ. posth. Venice, 1598) quo. G. Severini, *Architettura militare di Giuliano da Sangallo* (Pisa, 1970) 52n.
37 Op. cit., 4–5.
38 Op. cit., 152–3.
39 Quoted by Judith Hook in an article to be published in *History*. I am grateful for having been able to see a draft.
40 E.g. Battista della Valle, *Vallo, libro contenente appartenentie ad capitanii* . . . (Naples, 1521) and Machiavelli, *Arte della guerra* (Florence, 1522).
41 Bartolomeo Scola, *Di Basilio della Scola* . . . (Vicenza, 1888) 15–33.
42 The former wrote *Delle fortificazione libri cinque* (Venice, 1596).
43 Aurora Scotti, *Ascanio Vitozzi ingegnere ducale a Torino* (Florence, 1969) 52.
44 Quoted by G. Ruscelli, *Precetti della militia* . . . (Venice, 1583) 40v.
45 Lynn White Jr, 'Jacopo Aconcio as engineer', *American Historical Review* (1967) 425–44. In his manuscript treatise of 1551 dedicated to Duke Cosimo I of Florence, Maggi explained how he had learned about 'architecture' (the term he always used for the design of fortifications) from visiting sites and questioning experts. Marciana library, Venice, Mss. It. Cl. IV, 42 = 5364,3.
46 Op. cit., 4.
47 Vasari, Life of Michelangelo, in *Lives* . . ., tr. G. Bull (London, 1971) 78.
48 Tr. cit., 135, 113, 87.
49 Op. cit., 18.
50 1593 seq.
51 Op. cit., 26v.
52 Buselli, op. cit., 60.
53 Decoration was possible only when fortifications were faced with solid materials. The employment of earth, reinforced with stakes and faced with turf was widespread; the weather has destroyed some of the most elaborate fortifications of the period; v. J.R. Hale, 'Francesco Tensini and the fortification of Vicenza', *Studi Veneziani* (1968) 231–89. The first full treatment of the subject to be printed was G. Lanteri, *Due libri del modo di fare le fortificazioni di terra* (Venice, 1559). Earthen works (and not only temporary field defences) were known as 'opere da soldato' or 'architettura

soldatesca'. V. L.A. Maggiorotti, *L'opera del genio italiano all'estero . . .* (3v., Rome, 1933–9) ii, 10–11.

54 Op. cit., 216.

55 *Storia delle fortificazioni nella spiaggia romana* (Rome, 1880) 67, 160, 181, 206–7.

56 *Miscellanea di Storia Italiana*, iv, 362.

57 'I will give you the exact proportions of a man. Those of a woman I will disregard, for she does not have any set proportion.' Cenino Cenini, *The Craftsman's Handbook,* tr. D.V. Thompson (Yale U.P., 1933) 48. This, however unfairly, continued to be the orthodox opinion.

58 Tr. cit., i, 12–15.

59 Quoted by James S. Ackerman, 'Architectural practice in the Italian Renaissance', *Journal of the [American] Society of Architectural Historians* (1954, no. 3) 3.

60 *On Technique*, cit., 96–8.

61 Op. cit., 190r.

62 Paolo Marconi, 'Una chiave per l'interpretazione dell' urbanistica rinascimentale. La citadella come microcosmo', *Quaderni dell'Istituto di Storia dell'Architettura* (1968) 64. And v. the same author's *La città come forma simbolica* (Rome, 1973).

63 C.R. Boxer and Carlos de Azevedo, *Fort Jesus and the Portuguese in Mombasa* (London, 1960) 109–17. The latter author's idea has not been followed, however, by James Kirkman, *Fort Jesus* (Oxford, 1974).

64 *Trattati*, ed. Corrado Maltese (2 vol., Milan, 1967) ii 431. Nor did the fortresses he actually built have anthropomorphic features, though fig. (1) shows how freely his plastic imagination could move away from his text.

65 Op. cit., 36–7.

66 E.g., Simon Pepper, 'The Meaning of the Renaissance Fortress', *Architectural Association Quarterly* (1973, no. 2) 22, 26. But the article is a valuable one for the moderation with which it urges a 'cultural' approach.

67 B. Varchi, *Storie Fiorentine* (3 vol.), Florence, 1843–4 i, 119.

68 Marconi, cit., *Città come forma . . .*, 76–80.

69 Bruschi, op. cit., 944. A footnote acknowledges the influence of Marconi.

70 Horst de la Croix, *Military Considerations in City Planning: Fortifications* (New York, 1972) 52. And cf. Simon Pepper, 'Planning Versus Fortification: Antonio da Sangallo's Plan for the Defence of Rome', *Architectural Review* (March, 1976).

71 James S. Ackerman, *The Architecture of Michelangelo* (London, 1970) 138.

72 Carlo Pedretti, *Leonardo da Vinci. The Royal Palace at Romorantin* (Cambridge, Mass., 1972) 34–5.

I am grateful for the suggestions made by Caroline Elam who was kind enough to read this lecture in draft.

LIST AND SOURCES OF ILLUSTRATIONS

Photographs are by the author unless an attribution is given.